SRI HAYAGRIVA STHOTHRAM

Sloka Work Book

JET Publishing House

INDIA   **USA**

TOWARDS EXCELLENCE

P
R
A
J
N
A

Title	SRI HAYAGRIVA STHOTHRAM
Subtitle	Sloka Work Book
Copyright	Jeeyar Educational Trust
First Edition	2013
Contributor	His Holiness Chinna Jeeyar Swamiji

CONTACT US:

<u>**INDIA**</u>	<u>**UNITED STATES**</u>
JIVA Sriramanagaram, Shamshabad, R.R. Dist. Andhra Pradesh - 509 325 Phone: 95535 49971, 95535 499	JETUSA Inc. Jeeyar Asram, 222, Dey Road, CRANBURY, NJ 08512, USA Phone:609-297-8797

Website: www.prajna4me.org   **Email:** prajna@jetusa.org

A Word

It is difficult to completely explain or even understand the different incarnations of Lord **S**riman-na:ra:ya**n**a, who appeared for the welfare of mankind. Each incarnation has its own significance.

Innumerable are the avatha:ras, the appearances of Lord on this earth, for uplifting mankind from miseries.

Lord **S**ri: Ra:ma exemplifies the greatest human qualities like truthfulness & affability. In the avatha:ra of Para**s**ura:ma, he demonstrates the need for the eradication of diabolic nature. **S**ri:Va:mana:vatha:ra, on the other hand, shows how Lord supports and protects de:vathas.

Some avatha:ras like Mathsya the divine fish, Vara:ha, the Sacred Boar, Hamsa, the White Swan and Lord ayagri:va, the divine horse-necked one, appeared to bless humans with knowledge and some showed how that knowledge can be implemented to protect virtues on earth.

Though we are not able to know everything about all these avatha:ras, we must learn about the incarnation of Hayagri:va, which appeared for the distribution of divine knowledge. Let us learn about its significance.

Hayagri:va has His neck like a horse and the body like a human. Just like the Nrusimha:vatha:ra, the form of Hayagri:va is stupendous and surprising. We all know that the ways of God are mysterious, pleasant and wonderful! Sage Ve:da Vya:sa explained about **S**ri: Hayagri:va in 2.7.11 and 5.18.6 of *Srimad Bha:gavatha* and also in the 11th canto. Even *Na:ra:yani:yam of Sa:nthi Parva* explains the significance of this avatha:ra!

At the time of creation, Lord **S**ri:manna:ra:yana taught the Holy Ve:das to the four headed Bramha. While Bramha was being preached, the four Ve:das appeared in the form of four Ve:da Purushas - human beings. But, Bramha did not pay attention. Paying a deaf ear to one's teacher is a great sin! As a result, two demons Madhu and Kaitabha emerged from a drop of sweat that formed at the Lord's navel.

These demons tried to steal the Ve:das from Bramha. All the four Ve:da Purushas fought on behalf of Bramha, but they were of no match for the two demons. The demons carried the Ve:da Purushas away to the underworld, *rasa:thala*, leaving Bramha in his own world.

What happens when light is lost? There will be darkness. Similarly, having lost the light of knowledge and surrounded by darkness, Bramha prayed to the Lord and performed a great *yajna* to get blessed by the Lord again with the knowledge of the Ve:das. Lord **S**ri:manna:ra:ya**n**a, who is compassionate, took pity on Bramha and went to the underworld *rasa:thala* in the form of Hayagri:va and neighed loudly.

The stentorian voice of Lord Hayagri:va frightened the demons and made them run helter - skelter in horror. Then, Lord Hayagri:va brought the Ve:da Purushas carefully from the underworld and appeared from the fire altar of the yajna that Bramha was performing. He blessed Bramha, who prayed earnestly for the divine knowledge again with the Ve:das. The neighing of Lord Hayagri:va resembles *udgi:ttha*, the music of *Sa:ma Ve:da.*

The demons who had run away previously, returned and searched for the Ve:da Purushas. As they failed to find them in the place where they hid them, they left for Vaikun**tt**a, the abode of Lord Vishnu, wondering if they had been rescued by Him. Foolishly, they challenged Lord Vishnu for a fight and ended up losing their lives. But, Lord Vish**n**u is so compassionate that He cannot ignore even those that fight Him. He blessed them with salvation in spite of their sins.

As Bramha obtained the Vedic knowledge with all earnestness, he was able to retain it with him forever without any disturbance. That's why it is said that 'nothing should be taught without being requested'. Lord Vishnu created Bramha on the day of prathipath or pa:dyami, the 1st day after new moon and preached him the divine knowledge of the Ve:das. As it all went futile, it has been suggested that a new lesson should not be taught or learnt on *prathipath* or *pa:dyami* day, i.e.,the first day after new moon or full moon.

Since the Lord appeared on **S**ra:vana Pu:r**n**ima, in the holy fire of yajna, He feels specially pleased with all our prayers on that day and blesses us with all love and compassion, as it is His birthday. He removes all our obstacles and blesses us with the most powerful and the greatest knowledge, which helps us achieve great results.

Our elders say that Lord Hayagri:va is the embodiment of all knowledge. *Haya* means knowledge and *gri:va* means the neck. Lord Hayagri:va is thus the personification of all divine knowledge.

The four Ve:da:s – *Ruk, Yajus, Sa:ma and Attharva* are the source for all knowledge in the world. They are in the form of *manthras*, the holy chants with very powerful sounds. These manthras contain *bi:ja:ksharas*, vital letters. The entire energy of the manthra lies in these *bi:ja:ksharas*. The *bi:ja:ksharas* are subtle and indistinctive unlike the *manthras*. They do not appear meaningful, but possess excellent power. These *bi:ja:ksharas* are called

uththama:nga of the *manthras*. '*uththama:nga*' means head. If we personify the manthras, Hayavadana is the head similar to the *bi:ja:ksharas* of the *manthras*.

It is difficult to guess the meaning of a horse's neighing! The meaning of the neighing of this great Hayavadana also appears to be inexplicable, but it has a divine meaning. It is very powerful like the bi:ja:ksharas. It eradicates all evils and hence the evil and diabolic forces ran hither and thither.

Though we are not able to chant all the *manthras* and the hidden *bi:ja:ksharas*, a sincere prayer to Lord Hayagri:va, the embodiment of all divine knowledge, will bring us all the power of learning. Sri Ve:da:ntha De:sika composed *Hayagri:va Stho:thra* in thirty three verses explaining the significance of Lord Hayagri:va.

The whole divine world of de:vathas has thirty three divisions. Similarly, the total number of letters in the holy *manthras ashta:kshari: & dwaya manthra* also are thirty three. The divine energy of each letter was embedded by *Sri Ve:da:ntha De:sika* in each verse. This was experienced by great scholars. Hence, this great *stho:thra* was revered by profound scholars in the past and also is being revered in the present for a great eloquence and powerful speech.

Let all the enthusiastic scholars and students chant these powerful verses for a great power ful eloquent speech with a strong grip on the words and their meanings through the benediction of Lord Hayagri:va!

Jai Srimanna:ra:yana!

Telugu	Hindi	English	Telugu	Hindi	English
అ	अ	a	ట	ट	ta
ఆ	आ	a:	ఠ	ठ	tta
ఇ	इ	i	ఠ	ट	**tta**
ఈ	ई	i:	డ	ड	**da**
ఉ	उ	u	డ్డ	ड्ड	**dda**
ఊ	ऊ	u:	ధ	ढ	**dha**
ఋ	ऋ	ru	ణ	ण	**na**
ౠ	ॠ	ru:	త	त	tha
ఌ	अलु	lu	త్త	त्त	ththa
ౡ	अलू	lu:	థ్థ	त्थ	ttha
ఎ		e	థ	थ	
ఏ	ए	e:	ద	द	da
ఐ	ऐ	ai	ద్ద	द्द	dda
ఒ		o	ధ	ध	dha
ఓ	ओ	o:	న	न	na
ఔ	औ	au/ow	ప	प	pa
అం	अं	am	ఫ	फ	pha
అః	अः	aha	బ	ब	ba
క	क	ka	భ	भ	bha
ఖ	ख	kha	మ	म	ma
గ	ग	ga	య	य	ya
ఘ	घ	gha	ర	र	ra
ఙ	ङ	nga	ల	ल	la
చ	च	cha	వ	व	va
చ్చ	च	chcha	శ	श	sa
చ్	छ	chha	ష	ष	sha
చ	छ		స	स	sa
జ	ज	ja	హ	ह	ha
ఝ	झ	jha	ళ	ळ	la
ఞ	ञ	ini	ఱ		rra
			క్ష	क्ष	ksha
			జ్ఞ		Jna

* This letter comes only in the middle of the word
* * This letter comes in the beginning/middle of the word

☞ Pronounciation of both these letters is almost similar

PRAJNA PLEDGE

Jai Srimannarayana!

O Mother Earth! I, being your best child and responsible citizen of this world, take this pledge!

I shall revere my parents, my family, my Gurus and treat everyone with love.

I shell serve my community, my country and those in need.

I pledge to protect the Nature by caring for animals, trees and the environment.

I will learn from the experiences of my ancestors and pass it on to future generations.

I, as student of Prajna, swear to abide by the universal commandments.

**Worship your own and Respect all &
Serve all beings as service to God.**

Jai Srimannarayana!

CONTENTS

Introduction

I. Choose the correct answer

1.   Hayagri:va Stho:thra was written by
    a.   Sage Va:lmi:ki
    b.   Ve:dantha De:sika
    c.   Sage Na:rada
    d.   None of the above

2.   Hayagri:va has a
    a.   lion body
    b.   human body
    c.   fish body
    d.   tortoise body

3.   In Bha:gavatham, Hayagri:va is referred in
    a.   2nd, 8th cantos
    b.   3rd, 9th, 11th cantos
    c.   2nd, 5th, 11th cantos
    d.   3rd, 5th, 11th cantos

4.   Lord blessed Bramha with
    a.   money
    b.   world
    c.   Ve:das
    d.   garland

5.   Madhu and Kaitabha were
    a.   de:vathas
    b.   yakshas
    c.   men
    d.   asuras

6.   Ve:das took the form of
    a.   de:vathas
    b.   asuras
    c.   yakshas
    d.   humans

7.   The asuras were _____ in the war against Lord Hayagri:va.
    a.   defeated
    b.   imprisoned
    c.   killed
    d.   victorious

8.   Lord appeared as Mathsya avatha:ra
    a.   to rescue the species
    b.   to bless the king
    c.   to live in water
    d.   none of the above

9.   Lord incarnated as _____ to help de:vathas.
    a.   Parasura:ma
    b.   Va:mana
    c.   Krushna
    d.   all of the above

10.   Which day is prathipath?
    a.   10th day after Pu:rnima
    b.   10th day after Ama:va:sya
    c.   1st day after Ama:va:sya and Pu:rnima
    d.   None of the above

11. _____ gave Ve:das back to Bramha.
    a.   Madhu
    b.   Kaitabha
    c.   Hayagri:va
    d.   None

12.   Hayagri:va's neigh resembled the sound of
    a.   Flute
    b.   Violin
    c.   Udgi:ttha
    d.   Ruk

13.   Bramha was born on
    a.   Pu:rnima
    b.   Ama:va:sya
    c.   Pa:dyami
    d.   None of the above

14.   Sa:sthra says to impart Ve:dic knowledge to those who
    a.   deserve it
    b.   want it
    c.   everyone
    d.   no one

15.   Ve:da Purushas were kept hostage in
    a.   Heaven
    b.   Hell
    c.   Vaikuntta
    d.   Nether worlds

16.   The first time, Lord imparted Ve:das to Bramha on
    a.   Pu:rnima
    b.   Ama:vasya
    c.   Pa:dyami
    d.   None

17.   Hayagri:va appeared on
    a.   Sra:vana Pu:rnima
    b.   Vaisa:kha Pu:rnima
    c.   Ka:rthi:ka Pu:rnima
    d.   None of the above

18. The power of manthra lies in
    a. bi:ja:ksharas
    b. all the letters
    c. God
    d. none of the above

19. Uththama:nga of a manthra is
    a. Pura:nas
    b. Bi:ja:ksharas
    c. Upanishads
    d. Ve:das

20. Pu:rnima is also called
    a. Pournami
    b. Prathipath
    c. Pa:dyami
    d. None of the above

II. Put in sequence

1. Asuras took the Ve:da purushas to the nether world.

2. Bramha was inattentive.

3. Lord took the form of Hayagri:va.

4. Lord took pity on Bramha.

5. Lord blessed the demons with salvation.

6. Asuras came back and fought with Vishnu.

7. Hayagri:va neighed.

8. Lord taught Ve:das to Bramha on prathipath.

9. Lord defeated the asuras.

10. Bramha performed a great yajna seeking Ve:das from Lord.

11. Lord awarded them mo:ksham.

12. Lord appeared from the ritual fire on **Sra:vana Pu:rnima**.

13. Lord blessed Bramha with Ve:das.

14. Bramha lost the light of knowledge.

15. Bramha was grief-stricken.

III. Analogy

1. Udgi:ttha is to Sa:ma Ve:da :: Ruks is to _____ .

2. Horse face is to Hayagri:va :: _____ is to Narasimha.

3. Uththama:nga is to _____ :: Upanishads is to Ve:dic knowledge.

4. _____ is to Hayagri:va Stho:thra :: Ve:da Vya:sa is to Maha:bha:ratha.

5. Lotus is to Bramha :: _____ is to Vishnu.

6. Prathipath is to one :: E:ka:dasi is to _____

7. Bha:drapada Ashtami is to Krushna :: _____ is to Hayagri:va.

8. De:vathas is to 33 divisions :: Hayagri:va Stho:thra is to

   _____

9. Holy fire is to Hayavadana :: lotus is to _____

10. Mathsya:vatha:ra is to save all species :: Parasura:ma is to _____ the rulers.

IV.   Match the Following

1.	Four men	a.	Maha:bha:ratha
2.	Manthram	b.	Four Ve:das
3.	Hayagri:va appeared	c.	Fire altar
4.	Uththama:ngam	d.	Bi:ja:ksharam
5.	Sra:vana Pu:rnima day	e.	Lord's Neigh
6.	Eradicator of evils	f.	Head
7.	Sa:nthi Parva	g.	Hayagri:va's birthday

V. Answer the Following

1.   What is an 'avatha:ra'?

2.   What is the purpose of Hayagri:va avatha:ra?

3.   A disciple should be attentive. why?

4.   Why did Bramha lose Ve:das?

5.   Why did asuras go to the milky ocean?

6.   Which avatha:ras of Lord are awe-inspiring?

7.   Why did Ve:dic knowledge remain with Bramha?

8.   Why is pa:dyami not suited to start a new lesson?

VI.   Draw

1.   Madhu and Kaitabha stealing Ve:das

2.   Four Ve:da Purushas

3.   Mathsya:vatha:ra

VII. Project

Create a model of ho:ma kunda – fire altar.

Slo:ka 1

I. Choose the correct answer

1.   Knowledge is favorable to us because it
    a.   fulfills our desires
    b.   gives us power
    c.   gives us health
    d.   gives us wealth

2.   'Nirmala' means
    a.   spotless
    b.   cool
    c.   hot
    d.   white

3.   Hayagri:va's form glows like a
    a.   star
    b.   diamond
    c.   glass
    d.   white spotless crystal

4.   Hayagri:va's effulgence surpasses the brightness of
    a.   the sun and the moon
    b.   a 10000 watt light
    c.   the sun
    d.   all the planets

5.   Lord Hayagri:va is the personification of
    a.   knowledge
    b.   bliss
    c.   crystal
    d.   a&b

6. Choose the correct statement
   a. Lord Hayagri:va is lion necked God
   b. Lakshmide:vi sits on His right lap
   c. Lord Hayagri:va holds sankha in His right hand
   d. Lakshmide:vi sits on His left lap

7. Ithiha:sas are
   a. Srimad Ra:ma:yana
   b. Srimad Maha:bharatham
   c. All pura:nas
   d. a & b

8. One among the below is a Pura:na
   a. Srimad Ra:ma:yana
   b. Srimad Maha:bharatham
   c. Srimad Bha:gavatham
   d. none of the above

II. Match the words with their meanings

1. de:vam   a. eternal knowledge

2. jna:nam   b. source

3. a:nandam   c. bright God

4. a:dha:ram   d. eternal happiness

5. sphatika   e. white crystal

III. Choose the correct word and fill in the blanks

1. Lord Hayagri:va is _____ . (jna:na:nanda mayaha, upa:smahe:).

2. He is _____. (de:vaha, mayam).

3. His form is like _____ .(nirmala sphatikam, upa:smahe:).

4. He is the source of _____. (a:kruthim, sarva vidya:ha)

5. I _____ Hayagri:vam. (upa:smahe:, a:dha:ram)

IV. Fill in the missing letters

1. N ___ R ___ ___ L ___

2. S ____ ____ ___ T ____ ____ A

3. ____ N ____ : N ____

4. A ___ N ___ ____ D ___

5. S ____ ____ ___ A

V. Answer the following

1. What gives us happiness?

2. Why do we address the Lord as 'de:va'?

3. Why do we meditate on Lord Hayagri:va?

4. Describe the radiance of Lord Hayagri:va.

5. Write the meaning of the first slo:ka in your own words.

VI. Learn More – Slo:ka Picture Introduction

Goda	–	Vishnu, what are these around Lord Hayagri:va?
Vishnu	–	Mmm…. I think they are some books.
Goda	–	What books Vishnu?
Vishnu	–	Don't know. Lets ask Grandpa.
Kids	–	Grandpa! Grandpa!
Grandpa	–	Jai Srimannarayana Kids! Whats up?
Goda	–	We have a question Grandpa!
Vishnu	–	Grandpa, we are learning Hayagri:va Stho:thram.
Goda	–	And we are trying to understand the picture of this first slo:ka. Can you explain what it means?

Grandpa	–	Well, let me see it. It is a picture of Lord and various scriptures.
Go:da	–	But, why did they draw the scriptures around the Lord, Grandpa?
Grandpa	–	Lord Hayagri:va is the treasure house of infinite knowledge. Various scriptures are shown around the Lord to show that.
Go:da	–	I hear this word 'scripture' many times. What does it mean?
Vishnu	–	A scripture is a book! Obviously!
Go:da	–	So is any book a scripture?
Vishnu	–	Oh, well I'm not sure. Grandpa??
Grandpa	–	A scripture is a sacred or a holy book. It is divine.
Go:da	–	Who wrote them Grandpa?
Grandpa	–	Great sages, saints, and a:cha:ryas wrote them. The only exception is Ve:das. They are Ve:das were not written by anyone.
Go:da	–	Can you tell us more about scriptures?
Grandpa	-	Sure. The whole mass of Ve:das was classified into 4 parts with 1131 branches by great sage Ve:da Vyasa. We have Upanishads which are part of Ve:das. Pura:nas were written by the great Sage Ve:da Vya:sa, and Sage Para:sara, the father of Ve:da Vya:sa. A:gamas are texts which describe the process of worshipping God and de:vathas. Smruthis, Dharmasa:stras, Ve:da:ngas, and many more scriptures… All these were written by sages.
Vishnu	-	What about Ra:ma:yana and Maha:bha:ratha?
Grandpa	-	Vishnu! I was just about to tell you. Ithiha:sas are our history. Ra:ma:yana and Maha:bha:ratha are ithiha:sas. They are histories of the world that happened ages ago. Bhagavad Gi:tha is a part of Maha:bha:ratha too.
Go:da	-	Who wrote them?

Grandpa	-	Ra:ma:yana was written by Sage Va:lmi:ki .Maha:bha:ratha was documented by Sage Ve:da Vya:sa.
Vishnu	-	Is that all?
Grandpa	-	No. So far, we only discussed about the contributions of sages. We have scriptures handed over to us by great saints whom we call a:lwa:rs.
Grandpa	-	They sang about 4000 songs in Tamil which are called Divya Prabandham.
Go:da	-	What did A:cha:ryas write Grandpa?
Grandpa	-	They wrote many commentaries on the above. Our Ve:dic literature is very rich in culture, heritage, knowledge and tradition. These scriptures teach us how a human being should conduct with himself, his family, the society around him, how to live harmoniously with Nature and ultimately how to reach the final goal.
Go:da	-	But why are there many scriptures with this information?
Grandpa	-	Well, as time goes on, man is growing weak with memory. Man could once remember all the above. However, now, we are finding it difficult to even remember a few phone numbers!
		Now kids, go and make a chart listing these scriptures.
Kids:	-	Sure Grandpa!
Grandpa	-	Thus, our a:cha:ryas have simplified the vast Ve:dic knowledge in many ways.
		And our Chinna Jeeyar Swamiji and other gurus talk about these scriptures in their discourses in the most simple language to make us understand.

Try to make a chart of all the scriptures. Anyway, you will be learning more about it in Module 5.

I. Questions on Slo:ka Picture

1.   List the four Ve:das from the picture.

2.   List the 18 Pura:nas mentioned in the picture.

3.   What other scriptures are shown in the picture.

VII. Do you remember?

1.   Who wrote Pura:nas?

2.   Who branched Ve:das into four categories?

3.   Name the place where the sage worked on these scriptures.

VIII. Group Discussion

Form a group of 3-4 students for this exercise. Discuss the topic within your own group for 10 -15 minutes, gather the ideas and present them methodically to the whole Prajna class. One person can represent a group. List five reasons – Why or Why not.

Topic for discussion — 'Knowledge is Power'

IX.   Criss Cross Puzzle

Across

3. number of ve:da:ngas

4. number of slo:kas in Hayagri:va stho:thra

5. number of Gods

Down

1. number of pura:nas

2. number of Ve:das

X. Research

1.   How do you say the word 'knowledge' in different langages

2.   Different kinds of crystals and their formations.

3   Two famous Sanskrit sayings on Knowledge/scholar along with their meanings in English.

Slo:ka 2

I. Choose the correct answer

1. Hayagri:va's radiance competes with
   a. the lamp
   b. a huge gem mountain
   c. a star
   d. none of the above

2. His radiance spreads across
   a. the heaven
   b. the earth
   c. skies
   d. all the three worlds

3. Lord Hayagri:va
   a. removes evil qualities
   b. blesses only few people
   c. appears like a gold mountain
   d. none of the above

4. The Upanishads
   a. follow Hayagri:va's neigh
   b. follow Indra
   c. ignore the Lord
   d. none of the above

5. Chant this slo:ka to get
   a. money
   b. good education
   c. memory power
   d. good health

II. Choose the correct word and fill in the blanks

1. Lord Hayagri:va appeared _____ .(bhu:bruth, swathaha)

2. His radiance competes with _____ (bhu:bhruth, sudha:) of spotless gems.

3. Upanishads followed His _____. (thrayyanthaihi, he:sha: halahalam).

4. He destroys the _____ (ananthaihi, avadyam) of all devotees.

5. We praise the _____ (mahaha hayavadanam, ase:sha)

III. True or False

1. Hayagri:va's form is like a pink mountain.

2. All the three worlds are illuminated by Him.

3. Hayagri:va follows the Upanishads.

4. Lord removes the drawbacks of his devotees.

5. We pray to the great effulgence of Lord Hayagri:va.

IV. Answer the following

1. Why did Lord Hayagri:va take a visible form?

2. How is Lord Hayagri:va described in this slo:ka?

3. How does Lord bless the three worlds?

4. What removes the defects of all devotees?

5. Mention the benefits of meditating on this slo:ka

V. Match the following

1.	thrayyanthaihi	a.	countless
2.	avadha:tha	b.	on his own
3.	ananthaihi	c.	shining
4.	swathaha	d.	we praise
5.	i:di:mahi	e.	upanishads

VI. Complete Criss Cross Puzzle with equivalent Sanskrit words.

Across

5. world
6. three
7. divine glow

Down

1. pure
2. glow radiating from white plastering
3. gem
4. which destroys
8. defects

VII. Group Discussion

Form a team of 3-4 students for this exercise. Take 30 minutes to do the exercise and present your ideas to the whole class.

1. Why is education important?

2. Discuss what good education means?

3. Is education limited to books only?

4. What are the hurdles to get good education?

5. Five things you can do to get good education.

6. How can you improve the existing educational system?

VIII. Unscramble

HIRT   ☐☐☐☐

HATHA   ☐☐☐☐☐

HADDSU   ☐☐☐☐☐☐

HAAMAH   ☐☐☐☐☐☐

RATPIH   ☐☐☐☐☐☐

IX. Learn More

Grandpa	–	Jai Srimannarayana Kids!
Kids	–	Jai Srimannarayana grandpa.
Go:da	–	Grandpa, I have a question for you.
Grandpa	–	Go ahead.
Go:da	–	In Hayagri:va stho:thra – there is a word "thribhuvanam" which means three worlds…
Vishnu	–	What are they and where do they exist?

Grandpa   –   Good question. 'thribhuvanam' means three worlds. They are u:rdhva lo:ka, bhu: lo:ka and adho: lo:ka.

Bhu:lo:ka is earth. Anything we see above earth is called u:rdhva lo:ka. And anything relatively below is called adho:lo:ka. According to our scriptures, there is a setup for this universe. These worlds rotate on their orbits at different speeds just like the solar family. The setup of these worlds never changes.

Go:da   –   Grandpa, we often hear about swarga, heaven. Where is it?

Grandpa   –   Well, U:rdhva lo:ka infact has seven lo:kas i.e worlds. All these worlds are clubbed together and called u:rdhva lo:ka. Swarga lo:ka is one among them. Similarly, adho:lo:ka has seven worlds.

Go:da   –   Does anyone live in these worlds?

Grandpa   –   Why not, our scriptures clearly tell us that souls live in these worlds. However, their bodies are different from ours. The souls which live in the u:rdhva lo:kas have 'the:jas sariras' to enjoy the benefits of good deeds they did in their previous births. The souls in the adho: lo:kas undergo punishments for the bad deeds they did in their previous births.

Vishnu   –   Thanks grandpa for giving this wonderful insight into the three worlds.

X. Debate

'Ignorance is Bliss'

XI.   Writing Project

Imagine you and your friends are trekking the Hima:laya mountains. Among the mountain ranges, all of a sudden you saw a pure crystal mountain shining brilliantly. How would you feel?

XII.   Workshop

1.   Go to a pitch dark room. Is anything visible? Now, light a lamp. What happens? Can you relate it to knowledge?

2.   Imagine you went on a trip to Japan. All the sign boards, directions etc., are written in Japanese. You are hungry and walked into a restaurant. Being a vegetarian, how would you order?

   Now, imagine that you were aware of your trip to Japan. You went to Japanese language classes and learnt a little Japanese. How different would your experience be now?

   What are your conclusions?

XIII. Know

Find the names of the following animals in Sanskrit – Horse, cow, buffalo, snake, tiger, lion, goat, cat, dog, elephant.

XIV.   Research

1.   Mountains – sources of gold in scriptures and modern days.

2.   Flying mountains

XVI. Names of at least five Upanishads

Slo:ka 3

I. Choose the correct answer

1. Lord's neigh eradicates
   a. good nature
   b. devilish nature
   c. impish nature
   d. playful nature

2. Wise people
   a. must enlighten the dull with knowledge
   b. are not pretentious
   c. have no doubts
   d. all of the above

3. _____ is the destroyer of obstacles.
   a. Lord Hayagri:va's neigh
   b. Bramha
   c. Indra
   d. Yama

4. Hayagri:va's neigh represents the
   a. songs of Sa:maveda
   b. Rug Ve:da hymns
   c. sonorous music of Ve:das
   d. none of the above

5. Perverted
   a. create doubts in minds of people
   b. misdirect the ordinary folk with wrong arguments
   c. create lot of commotion and disturbance in the community
   d. all the above

6. Lord Hayavadana
    a. clears the hurdles
    b. gives proper knowledge
    c. enlightens all
    d. all the above

7. Hayagri:va's neigh is like
    a. the sound of rain
    b. the waves in the ocean of knowledge
    c. harsh and shrill
    d. none of the above

8. The ruks of Rugve:da
    a. praise the de:vathas
    b. are musical hymns
    c. have sacrificial formulae
    d. none of the above

9. Lord's voice is the abode of
    a. Yajur Ve:da
    b. Upanishads
    c. obstacles
    d. yajnas

10. Choose the correct statement.
    a. Lord Hayagri:va is personification of Ve:das.
    b. Lord Hayagri:va protects us from ignorance.
    c. Lord Hayagri:va is destroyer of obstacles.
    d. All of the above.

II. Match the following

1. Rugve:da   a. sacrificial formulae
2. Sa:mave:da   b. praising verses
3. Yajurve:da   c. collection of tunes

III. Fill in the blanks with proper words from slo:ka

Lord Hayagri:va! The reverberations of your neigh is

_ ;

_ ;

_____ ;

_ ;

_____ ;

IV. Choose the correct word and fill in the blanks

1. Let your 'he:sha:' dispel the _____
    (anthardhwa:ntham, kattha)

2. Commotion is caused by _____ (kshyubhyath, darpa) people
    out of _____(kshyubhyath, darpa).

3. The inner darkness is removed by _____ (bo:dha
    , sudha:)

V. Give Sanskrit words from the slo:ka

1. Ocean

2. Knowledge

3. Hymns of Rugve:da

4. Collection

VI. Answer the following

1. 'He:sha:' is lovely to hear. Why?

2. Why is 'he:sha' compared to ruk?

3. What is the purpose of this slo:ka?

4. Which Ve:da consists of sacrificial chants?

5. How do arrogant people create disturbance in the community?

VII. Unscramble

TAAKHT

DAAPR

HAAY

HALYAA

TAURAHH

VIII. Solve the puzzle with equivalent English words

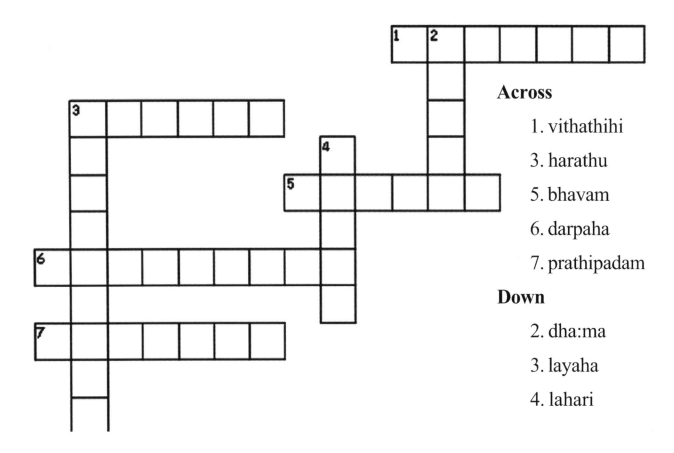

Across

1. vithathihi
3. harathu
5. bhavam
6. darpaha
7. prathipadam

Down

2. dha:ma
3. layaha
4. lahari

IX.   Learn More

Vishnu	-	Jai Srimannarayana Grandpa. Do you have some time?
Grandpa	-	Yeah sure. What do you want?
Go:da	-	Grandpa, have a question. What are Ve:das?
Vishnu	-	Go:da , don't you know? Ve:das are manthras, they are sounds.
Go:da	-	Yes, but what are those manthras about Grandpa?
Grandpa	-	Here it is… Rug Ve:da has manthras. These manthras praise de:vathas to please them. They are used to invite the de:vathas during yajnas and other divine occasions. Yajur Ve:da describes the process and procedures to conduct all kinds of yajnas and rituals. Sa:ma Ve:da is the source of sonorous tunes to please the invited de:vathas to fulfill our desires. And, Attharva Ve:da is a treasure mine having all the secrets of medicine, astronomy, black magic, aviation and many more sciences.
Vishnu	-	Astronomy! Are its roots also in Ve:das? Oh my god! I can't believe it!
Grandpa	-	Yes Vishnu , our Ve:das revealed a lot about astronomy and our sages were using the technology too. Unfortunately, we've lost it now.
Go:da	-	Grandpa, what about A:yurve:da or Dhanurve:da? Are they not Ve:das? Why didn't you mention them?
Grandpa	-	Well! Each ve:da has some branches in it – A:yurve:da, Gandharva Ve:da, Dhanur Ve:da are parts of the main Ve:das. Infact, Ve:das are the source of all kinds of sciences. Unfortunately, we lost the links.
Goda	-	Can we find them now?
Grandpa	-	Yes, we can. A lot of research is needed.
Vishnu	-	I will research on Ve:das when I grow big.
Grandpa	-	That will be awesome Vishnu!

X. Do you remember?

In Module 2 Prathas smarani:yam – you learnt about Ve:das and their branches.

1. Vedic knowledge was divided by whom and into how many categories?

2. What is the total number of branches?

3. How many branches exist today?

4. How many branches did Sa:ma Ve:da have? How many exist today?

5. List the number of branches in Rug Ve:da and how many exist today.

6. Yajur Ve:da had 101 branches. How many exist today?

7. How many branches were lost in Attharva Ve:da?

XI. Group Project

Record Ve:dic chantings of Rug Ve:da, Sa:ma Ve:da, Yajur Ve:da and Attharva Ve:da. Play them in the class. Do you find any difference in the chanting of the four Ve:das?

XII. Color the pictures

All our activities when offered to God become Yajna. Even eating food is a yajna. This yajna is called Anuya:ga. Hence, learned people never say "I ate food", instead they say "I took Anuya:ga". In each activity, you can visualize the homa kunda, fire, ghee, ho:tha (one who performs yajna), receiver i.e God.

Now, discuss with your classmates how feeding others is a yajna and present it in the class.

Ear –homa kunda

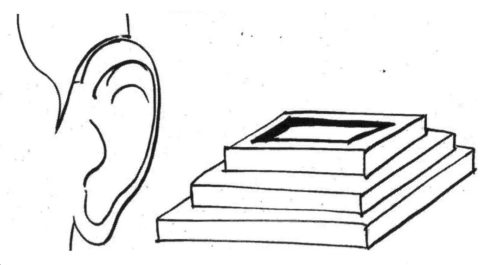

Hearing power – fire

Sounds – ghee

Sources of sounds – ho:thas

Recipient – God in us

Places, World – homa kunda

Objects, colors we see – fire

eye – hand of ho:tha:

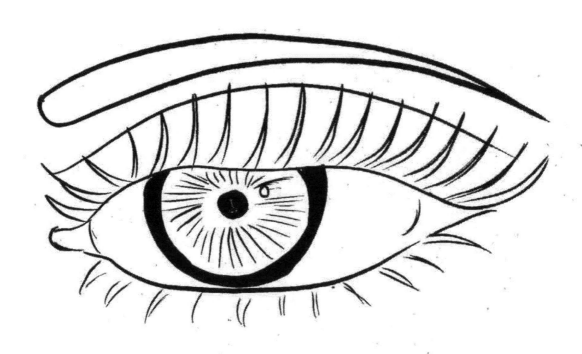

vision – ghee

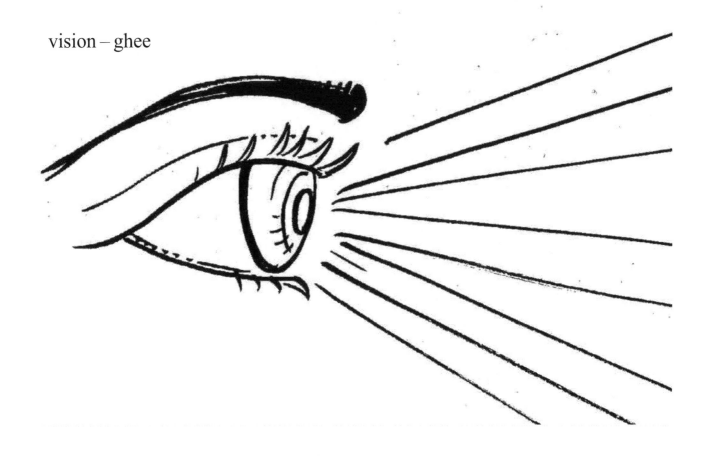

mouth – kunda

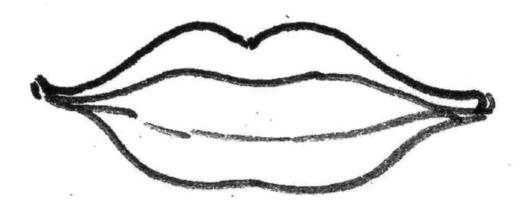

hunger – fire

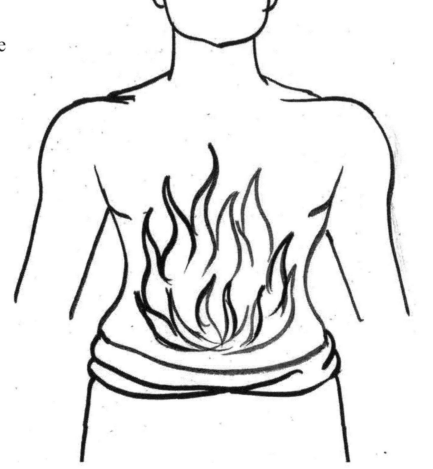

food – ghee

hotha – we through our hands

Recipient – god

any activity we do for a student

Teacher will be hotha

lesson – ghee

ears – fire

Recipients – God and our brain

XIII. Draw

We have many evil attitudes within us. These are like the demons which control our mind and actions making us bad people. Draw at least 10 similies showing evil attitudes typically found in most people.

XIV. Paragraph Writing

'Empty vessels make the most sound'.

XV. Research

Lord took many incarnations and one of them is Hayagri:va. Name a few (at least 3) other incarnations of Lord and write a small introduction about each incarnation.

Think of the neigh and you can modify your activities into ya:gas

Slo:ka 4

I. Choose the correct answer

1. Our ignorance is wiped off
   a. if we eat well
   b. if we sleep well
   c. if we meditate on Lord Hayagri:va
   d. if we do yo:ga

2. Ignorance is often compared to
   a. a huge mountain
   b. an ocean
   c. a dark night
   d. sunrise

3. The form of Lord is compared to
   a. eye-lining balm for the inner wisdom
   b. moon light
   c. torch light
   d. none of the above

4. The breath of Lord Na:ra:yana is
   a. Ve:das
   b. air
   c. oxygen
   d. all the above

5. Hayagri:va is an incarnation of
   a. Siva
   b. Bramha
   c. Indra
   d. Lord Sri:manna:rayana

II.   Choose the correct word and fill in the blanks

1.   Meditation on Lord Hayagri:va removes our mind's ignorance like=

_____

(pra:chi: sandhya:, va:ji vakthra:)

2.   He is like apu:rva: _____ (sandhya:, anjana sri:hi)

3.   His _____ (mu:rthihi,bha:thu) reveals _____ (prajna, ve:da:n)

III.   Correct the spellings

1.   vaktri

2.   bhatu

3.   drusehe

4.   kochit

5.   aparva

IV.   Answer the following

1.   What similies or metaphors are used in this slo:ka?

_____

_____

2.   What are we praying for in this slo:ka?

_____

_____

3.   Describe how Lord Hayagri:va removes our ignorance, using examples.

_____

_____

V. Solve the puzzle with meanings in English for the clues given below

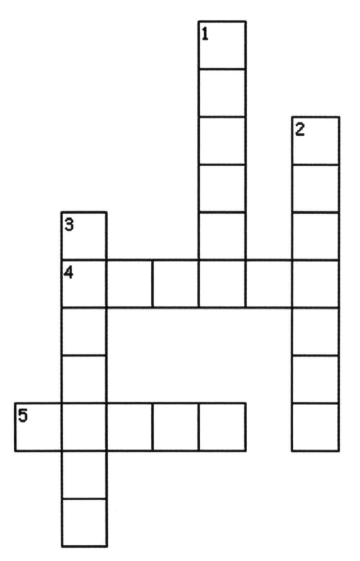

Across

4. bha:thu

5. Ve:da:n

Down

1. apu:rva:

2. sandhya:

3. pra:chi:

VI. Learn More

Grandpa   –   Children, what are you doing?

Vishnu and Go:da

  –   Jai Srimannarayana Grandpa. Our Prajna teacher asked us to research the meaning of word 'Ve:da' and create a poster on it. Can you help us?

Grandpa   –   Sure kids. Ve:da is a Sanskrit word. It is derived from the root "vid" which has two meanings -

1. 'to know' - ve:da ithi ve:daha , that which reveals all kinds of knowledge ve:ththi ane:na upa:ya:n ithi ve:daha, one who knows many means for becoming wise is Ve:da

2. 'to obtain' - vindathe: phala:n ane:na ithi ve:daha – obtaining good fruits through this, hence it is called Ve:da.

Go:da   –   Oh! So Ve:da means Knowledge through which we can obtain many things.

Grandpa   –   Yes. Go:da do you know that Ve:das are divided into 4 categories?

Vishnu   –   I know… I know them – Rug, Yajur, Sa:ma and Attharva Ve:da.

Grandpa   –   Good. Each Ve:da has three sections – Samhitha, Bra:mhanam, A:ranyakam

Go:da   –   Can you tell me more about them?

Grandpa   –   Later kids, meanwhile start working on your poster on Ve:das. I will see it when I come to visit you next time.

Vishnu   -   Sure grandpa. Jai Srimannarayana

Go:da   –   I am so excited. I will make a beautiful poster and show it to you. Jai Srimannarayana Grandpa.

VII. Speak on the below topic for 2 to 3 minutes

'I like Ve:da.'

VIII. Draw

In the stho:thra, you learnt that Ve:das are Lord's breath. The slo:ka in Sri: Vishnu Sahasrana:ma says – 'su:rya chandrau cha ne:thre' - The Sun and the Moon are His eyes. Visualize Lord's form and illustrate it.

IX.   Project

Prepare kohl at home and present it to your mother on Mother's Day or on her birthday.

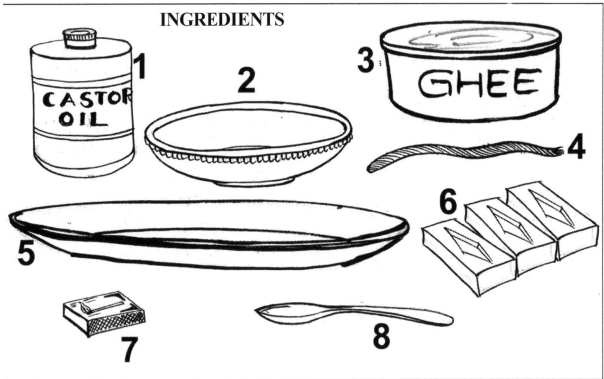

INGREDIENTS

1. 50 ml castor oil
2. 1 Big lamp that can accommodate 50 ml castor oil
3. Ghee
4. 1 long thick cotton wick.
5. copper plate
6. bricks
7. match box
8. spoon

Procedure

1

1. Pour castor oil into the lamp, put a wick and light the lamp.

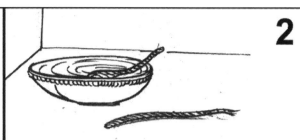

2

2. Place this lamp in a corner where there is no wind.

3

3. Take a big copper plate and apply castor oil to it.

4

4. Place the top of the plate such that it touches the flame of the lamp. It will approximately take 10 hours for the lamp to get extinguished.

5

5. When the oil is burnt, soot is deposited on the plate. This is the base of your kohl or eyeline.

6

6. Now using a spoon or any implement, scratch off the deposit. The soot is smooth, black, soft powder. Store it in an airtight container.

To make kohl Ⓐ

7

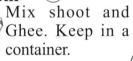 Mix shoot and Ghee. Keep in a container.

Ⓑ Dip your finger in the container which has the paste.

Ⓒ Rub it with your thumb for 5 seconds to make it consistent.

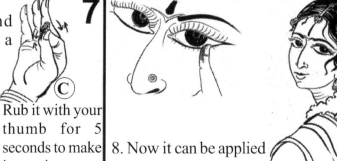

8

8. Now it can be applied to eyes.

Slo:ka 5

I. Choose the correct answer

1. Lord is the treasure house of
    a. anger
    b. compassion
    c. discipline
    d. none of the above

2. Lord Hayagri:va is the savior of
    a. mankind
    b. insects
    c. animals and birds
    d. all of the above

3. Defects often found in human knowledge
    a. one
    b. two
    c. three
    d. four

4. Misconception
    a. means mistaken belief
    b. is called Bhrama in Sanskrit
    c. is one of the deficiencies found in man
    d. all of the above

5. Prama:da means
    a. unattentive
    b. Misconception
    c. Deceiving others
    d. lack of abilities to understand or express

6. Lord Hayagri:va bestows
    a. false knowledge
    b. pure knowledge
    c. lot of wealth
    d. none of the above

7. Chant this slo:ka to get
    a. rid of ignorance
    b. rid of bad dreams
    c. rid of bad ideas
    d. rid of bad habits

8. Rohan did not complete his project. He is now planning to use his friend's project and claim that he did it. What is this attitude called?
    a. Bhrama
    b. Vipralipsa
    c. Asakthi
    d. Prama:da

9. Arjun goes on trekking. He sees a rope and thinks that it is a snake. What is this deficiency called?
    a. Bhrama
    b. Vipralipsa
    c. Asakthi
    d. Prama:da

10. Indu sits down to meditate but she cannot focus. What is this defect called?
    a. Bhrama
    b. Vipralipsa
    c. Asakthi
    d. Prama:da

II. Choose the correct word and fill in the blanks

1. I pray to Lord Hayavadana for He is _____ (visuddha vijna:na ghana, prapadye:)

2. He protects all creatures. Hence I meditate on _____ (vijna:na, daya: nidhim)

3. I _____ (prapadye:, saranyam) to Lord Hayagri:va.

4. Lord bestows _____ (swaru:pam, vijna:na)

5. Lack of concentration is called _____ (asakthi, prama:da)

III. Complete the slo:ka

_____ vijna:na ghana _____

Vijna:na _____ _____ di:ksham

_____ de:ha _____ _____

De:vam hayagri:vam _____ _____

IV. Answer the following

1. Understanding a concept with clarity is a boon. How can you get it?

2. What does misconception mean? Describe with examples.

3. Bramha suffered from one of the four defects and lost Ve:das. What is it?

4. List the four deficiencies in human knowledge with meanings and examples.

5. What results from asakthi?

V. Complete the puzzle with Sanskrit words for the clues given below

Across

  4. protector

  7. knowledge

  8. pure

  9. surrender

Down

  1. personification

  2. compassion

  3. form

  5. I

  6. treasure

VI. Unscramble

MAHA

AADY: ⊔⊔⊔⊔ :

NAHGA

DE:MAV ⊔⊔ : ⊔⊔⊔

HA:DE ⊔⊔ : ⊔⊔

VII. Correct the spellings

1. Divam
2. Surupam
3. Saranyam
4. Visiddha
5. Visranana

VIII. Illustrate the following

Bhrama, prama:da, vipralipsa, asakthi

IX. Workshop

1. Form a team of 3-4 students for this project. Let each group pick a story from Panchathanthra or any other fable which deals with one of the four defects – bhrama, prama:da, vipralipsa and asakthi and present it in the class using props.

2. Now discuss the disadvantages of having such defects.

3. Make a poster with a list of suggestions on how one can overcome these defects.

4. How the improved behavior impacts him and his surroundings?

X. Research

1. List famous personalities who fought with one of the four defects and overcame them successfully. Present their stories in the class.

2. Name the scripture which is free from all the four defects? Why?

Cumulative Exercises for Slo:kas 1 – 5

I. Analogy

1. Hayagri:va is to horse-necked God :: Narasimha is to _____.

2. Tunes is to Sa:ma Ve:da :: hymns is to _____

3. Bhrama is to _____ :: prama:da is to inattentiveness.

4. Vipralipsa is to _____ :: asakthi is to inability to perceive or express.

5. Hayagri:va's radiance is to suddha sphatikamani as His form is to *visuddha vijna:na gha*na_____

II. Find the odd man out

1. anjana, le:panam, parimala chu:rnam, thilakam, vasthraha

2. Ignorance, knowledge, diabolic attitudes, arrogance, pretention

3. bhrama, prama:da, bramha, vipralipsa, asakthi

4. Compassionate, savior, unswerving will, protector, ignorant

5. Asakthi, sphatika, sudha, jna:na

6. Mathsya pura:na, Vishnu pura:na, Bha:gavatham, Garuda pura:na, Ra:ma:yana

7. Rug, Sa:ma, Yajur, Attharva, Maha:bha:ratha

8. Si:ksha, vya:karana,cchandas, niruktha, kalpa, jyo:thisham, mi:ma:msa

9. Gold, sapphires, diamonds, corals, pearls

10. Zebra, boar, fish, lion, horse

III.   Match the following (pics)

1. Sphatika

2. Hayagri:vam

3. Anjana

4. Sandhya

5. Daya:nidhim

6. Prapadye:

7. Va:sude:va

8. Lahari

9. He:sha:

10. Thribhuvanam

11. Bhu:bruth

12. Mahaha

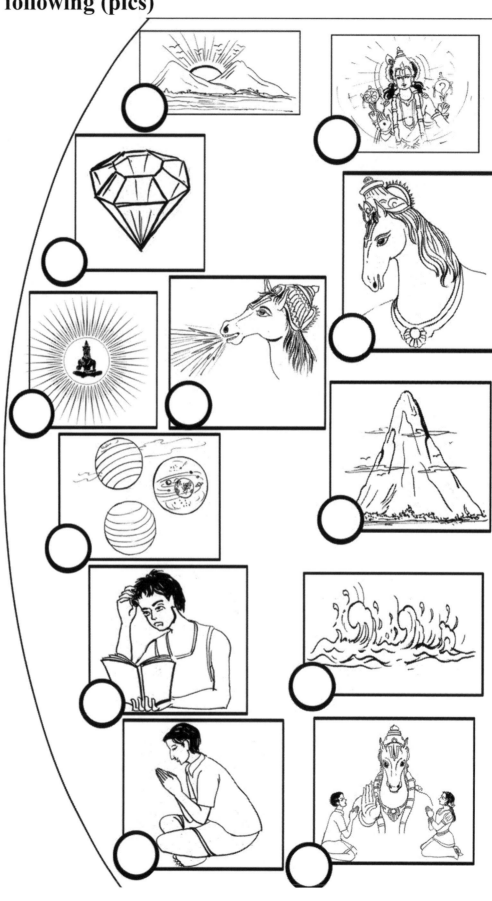

IV. Subhashitha:ni - Sanskrit Saying

na cho:raha:ryam na cha ra:ja ha:ryam na bhrathrubha:jyam na cha bha:raka:ri:
vyaye: kruthe: vardhatha e:va nithyam vidya:dhanam sarva dhana pradha:nam

Knowledge cannot be stolen by a thief.

Knowledge cannot be taken away by the rulers.

Knowledge cannot be divided among brothers.

Knowledge does not cause load. It grows by spending.

The wealth of knowledge is the greatest of all wealths.

Slo:ka 6

I. Choose the correct answer

1. Ve:da is called
   a. pourushe:yam
   b. apourushe:yam
   c. ka:vyam
   d. none of the above

2. Ve:das too failed to describe the
   a. qualities of Lord
   b. beauty of Lord
   c. compassion of Lord
   d. all of the above

3. "Lord! I am doing your stho:thram because _____"
   a. I am capable
   b. everyone can do it
   c. I know Sanskrit
   d. of my Love for you

II. True or False

1. Ve:das are anantham.

2. Ignorant people try to eulogize Lord.

3. Elders don't get angry on ignorant people.

4. Ve:das can describe the Lord's attributes.

5. Ve:das are partial.

6. Ve:das are the source of knowledge.

III. Choose the correct word and fill in the blanks

1. (stho:thras, apaurushe:yaihi) _____ with Ve:daihi, God is not reachable.

2. Oh! Hayagri:va! Consider me as a _____ (mugdhaha, bhu:thim) for eulogizing you.

3. I must be considered _____ (ka:runyathaha, sthuvan adya:pi)

IV. Correct the spellings

1. Apaurusheyas
2. Kata:kshaniyaha
3. Karunyatha
4. Bhouthim
5. prapachaih

V. Answer the following

1. Who composed Ve:da:s?
2. Can Ve:das describe the auspicious qualities of Lord fully? Why?
3. How do elders treat the ignorant kids?

VI. Solve the puzzle with equivalent Sanskrit words

Across

3. wealth

5. I

6. till date

7. lord

8. as

Down

1. by you

2. eulogize

4. innocent child

VII. Unscramble

DAYA

AIP

IIHT

KA:V

A:EV

HATWYA:

VIII. Learn More

Grandpa — Jai Srimannarayana children, today I am going to test you.

Vishnu — Oh no!

Go:da - Wow! grandpa. I love tests. Ask me! ask me!

Grandpa - In Module 2, you learnt the synonyms of Ve:das. What are they?

Go:da - sruthi, a:mna:ya:ha, apourushe:ya:ha, nirdushtam, aprame:yam

Vishnu - svathah prama:**n**am, **s**a:sthra, a:gama......,Don't remember the remaining ones. But do they all have the same meaning grandpa?

Grandpa - No. Now let us understand why they are called so.

sruthis - As they are passed on orally by word of mouth from teacher to the student. So it is sruthi – heard and learnt. It is a:mna:ya:m because Ve:da is memorized by repeated chanting

It is apourushe:ya:s as Ve:das are not written by anyone.

nirdushtam	–	Man written works may have some defects. Ve:da is apaurushe:ya. Hence no defects.
svathah prama:nam	–	It stands as authority for everything else and it didn't have any authority for its existence.
sa:sthra	–	Its an eternal command for dos and don'ts .
a:gama	–	it leads us to the ultimate goal of life.
ana:di nidhanam	–	eternal source of divine wealth.
nithyaha	–	Ve:da is timeless –exists past, present and future.
aprame:yam	–	Ve:da is beyond anyone's conception.

Kids   -   Thanks grandpa. Next time you test us, we will ace the test. Jai Srimannarayana

IX. Project

Write a poem or a paragraph on God on a poster. Decorate it and make a nice wall hanging. Write your name, Prajna class section and date on the bottom.

Do you think you were able to describe every aspect of God in your poem? Explain why.

X. Did you know?

Can you count the number of stars in the sky? Can you count the number of water drops in the oceans? Can you count the sand grains in a desert? Can you count the number of migrating birds in the sky? Can you count the number of droplets in the rain?

No.

Similarly, one cannot count the infinite 'kalyana gunas' - divine qualities of God. He has 'asankhye:ya kalya:na gunas' - infinite divine qualities.

Few say God is "nirguna" and interpet that God has no qualities. The word is right but the meaning has to be understood properly.

Ve:da and Upanishads described many qualities of God in many ways. They also said that God is not having limit to His greatness or has defective qualities like us. Our qualities are relative, expecting some response from others.

Hence the word nirguna should be explained as -

1. No bad qualities at all

2. His qualities are not similar to that of the souls.

In Sri Vishnu Sahasrana:ma Stho:thra, Bhi:shma:cha:rya says that God's qualities are multi dimensional and innumerable.

Pick any one quality of His and meditate on it. Visualize picturize and actualize it. You too will acquire that quality.

Slo:ka 7

I. Choose the correct answer

1. _____ impart knowledge.
   a. Ve:da Vya:sa Maharshi
   b. Dakshinamurthy
   c. Va:gde:vi
   d. All of the above

2. Va:gde:vi is _____ .
   a. Pa:rvathi
   b. Saraswathi
   c. Sathide:vi
   d. Si:tha

3. Bramha sits on a _____ .
   a. swan
   b. lion
   c. tiger
   d. lotus

4. Ve:davya:sa composed
   a. Sri: Ra:ma:yanam
   b. Pura:nas
   c. Raghuvamsam
   d. None of the above

5. _____ wrote Bramhasu:thras.
   a. Sage Vasishtta
   b. Bramha
   c. Sage Va:lmiki
   d. Sage Ve:da Vya:sa

II. Fill in the blanks with Sanskrit terms

1. Dakshina:murthy became great because of _____ (thava sakthi le:saihi, girisasya)

2. Va:gde:vi is _____ (vya:sa:dayo:pi, saro:ja:sana dharma pathni:)

3. Dakshina:murthy is the form of _____ (giri:sa, ramya, dakshina:)

III. Answer the following

1. Who is Dakshina:murthy?

2. How does Va:gde:vi bless her devotees?

3. Describe the contribution of Ve:da Vya:sa to the society.

4. Whom did Hayagri:va bless as initiators of knowledge?

5. What are we praying for in this slo:ka?

IV. Solve the puzzle using English words for the clues given below

Across

     3. girisasya

     5. ramya:

Down

     1. dharma pathni

     2. thava

     3. sphuranthi

     4. sarve:

     6. api

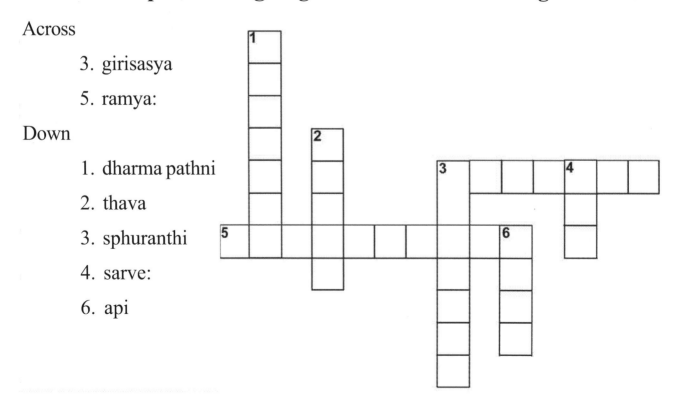

V. Unscramble

HTVAA ⬜⬜⬜⬜⬜

PIA ⬜⬜⬜

SAVRE: ⬜⬜⬜⬜⬜ :

RAYME: ⬜⬜⬜⬜⬜ :

AYV:SA ⬜⬜⬜ : ⬜⬜

TAKSIH ⬜⬜⬜⬜⬜⬜

MDHAAR ⬜⬜⬜⬜⬜⬜

VI. Learn More

Kids	-	Jai Srimannarayana Grandpa!
Grandpa	-	Jai Srimannarayana kids!
Vishnu	-	Grandpa, we learned today that Ve:da Vya:sa wrote Bramha Su:thras. What are they?
Go:da	-	Perhaps, life story of Bramha…
Grandpa	-	No, Bramhasu:thras is a scripture having 545 sentences.
Vishnu	-	What is the essence of them?
Grandpa	-	They reveal everything about Ve:dantha.
Go:da	-	Ve:dantha?
Grandpa	-	Ve:dantha – it is philosophy
Vishnu	-	Philosophy about what?
Grandpa	-	Philosophy about God, souls and nature.

Go:da	-	Grandpa! What are pura:nas?
Grandpa	-	Pura:nas are scriptures talking about the ancient history of life.
Vishnu	-	Ancient history?
Grandpa	-	Yes, all about its beginning, evolution and how it developed, who ruled, their lineages etc.
Goda	-	Wow! So evolution is also described in pura:nas.
Vishnu	-	Its so amazing to know that our sages were great scientists. Thanks grandpa for educating us about our scriptures. Jai Srimannarayana!

VIII. Group Discussion

Form a group of 3-4 students for this exercise. Discuss the below topic for 5 minutes. Note down your ideas. Now, let all the leaders of the groups discuss and present their conclusions to the class as a team.

Is God one or many?

VII. Write the names of their spouses

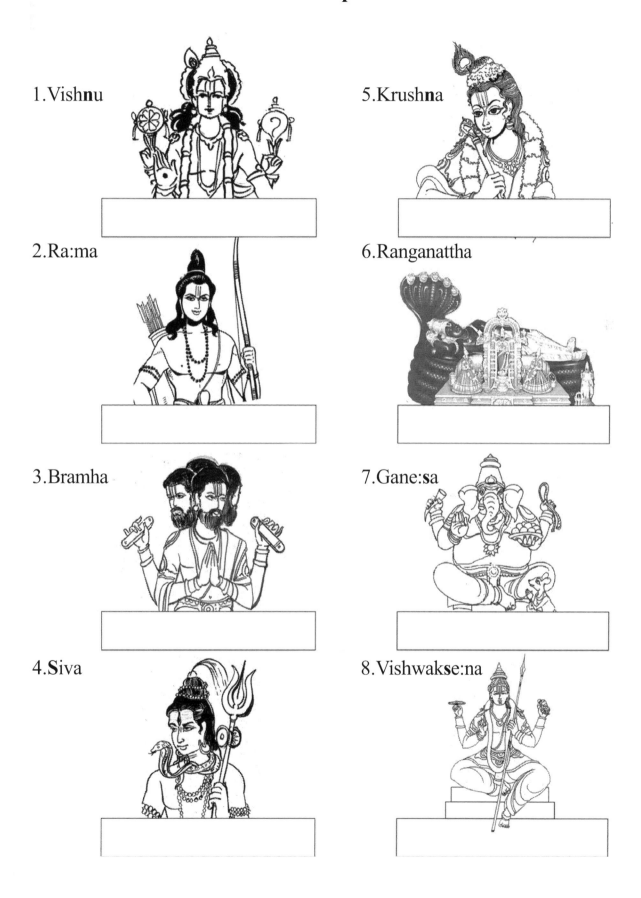

1.Vishnu

2.Ra:ma

3.Bramha

4.Siva

5.Krushna

6.Ranganattha

7.Gane:sa

8.Vishwakse:na

IX. Match the following with their musical instruments

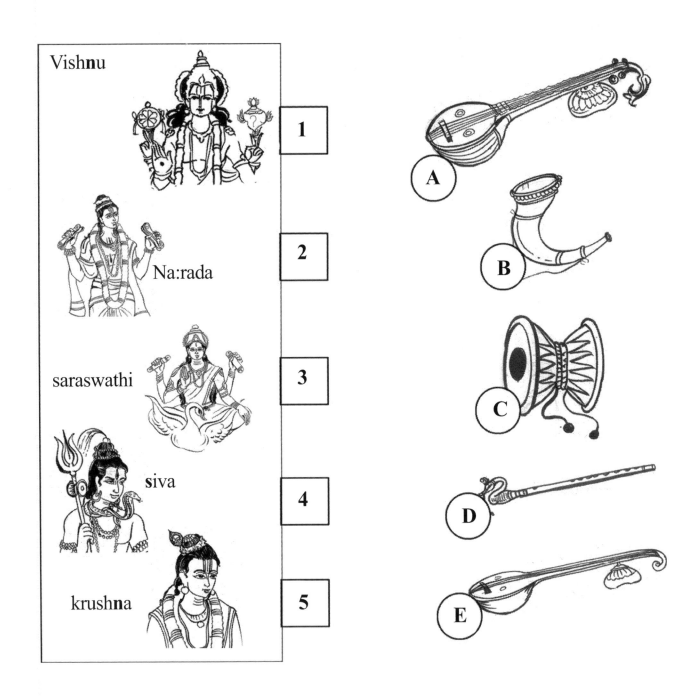

X. Draw the a:sanas of God and de:vathas

1. Na:ra:yana
2. Siva
3. Lakshmi De:vi
4. Saraswathi
5. Ka:rthike:ya
6. Bramha
7. Indra
8. Sri:Ra:ma and Si:thade:vi

XI. Do You Remember?

Sage Vya:sa had other names too. You learnt them in Module 1. Write the other names and describe

Slo:ka 8

I. Choose the correct answer

1. Bramha got Ve:dic knowledge
   a. in the beginning of creation
   b. during dwa:para yuga
   c. in the beginning of krutha yuga
   d. none of the above

2. Bramha felt _____ on losing Ve:das.
   a. unhappy
   b. happy
   c. relieved
   d. none of the above

3. Lord gave Ve:dic knowledge to Bramha in this incarnation
   a. Ra:ma
   b. Krushna
   c. Va:mana
   d. Hayagri:va

4. Bramha would have become _____ without Ve:das.
   a. dull headed
   b. a creator
   c. well-versed
   d. intelligent

5. Lord's _____ resulted in blessing Bramha with Ve:das again.
   a. compassion
   b. impatience
   c. anger
   d. patience

II. Choose the correct word and fill in the blanks

1. Oh! Lord! You _____ (niyatham, adhya:payishyaha)
   Ve:das that were _____(apani:tha:n, nigama:n) by the demons

2. Without Ve:das, Bramha would have been
   _____(mandaha, bhagadhe:yaha).

3. You taught Ve:das to Bramha _____(bhu:yo:pi, vanchitha).

4. Lord Hayagri:va, You are the _____ (nigama:n, va:cha:m nidhihi)

III. Answer the following

1. Why did Bramha lose Ve:das and how?

2. Why did Bramha become sad?

3. Who made Bramha knowledgeable?

4. What would have happened if Bramha did not get back Ve:das?

5. What are we praying for in this slo:ka?

IV. Match the following

1.	daithya	(a) lost Ve:das
2.	virinchaha	(b) stole Ve:das
3.	Hayavadana	(c) Ve:das
4.	nigama:n	(d) infinite grace

V. Correct the spellings

1. mandha

2. virunchaha

3. bhogadheyaha

4. bhuyapi

5. niryathum

VI. Solve the puzzle using Sanskrit words for clues given below

Across

    4. Bramha

    5. demons

Down

    1. for sure

    2. ignorant

    3. you

    4. deprived

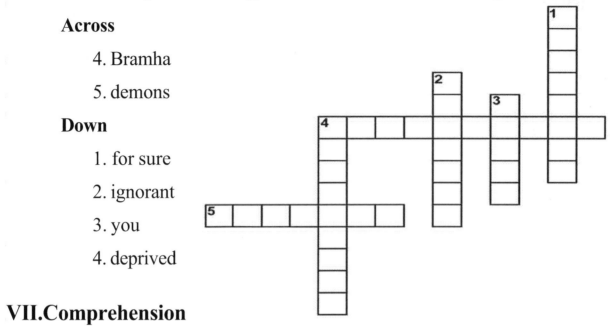

VII. Comprehension

A Good Student

Once Indra and Viro:chana approached Praja:pathi to gain knowledge. They prostrated before him and requested him to accept them as his disciples. Praja:pathi accepted them as his pupils.

Indra and Viro:chana stayed in the gurukulam for thirty two years and underwent severe austerities.

After thirty two years, Praja:pathi called his disciples and said, "Dear ones, I am happy with your sincerity. I will now reveal the eternal knowledge to you. Stand in front of a person and look into his eyes. Whomever you see in those eyes is God. He is the absolute truth." The disciples were very excited that their efforts have been fructified.

Viro:chana said, "Indra, come here. Stand in front of me". Indra did so and Virochana saw his own reflection in the eyes of Indra. Immediately, he thought " Oh God! I am the God" and was filled with pride. He rushed to his abode and ordered everyone to worship him only. He became uncontrollable and became asura.

Indra returned to heaven. He noticed that everyone was seeing their own

reflection in the eyes of others. He was not convinced that the reflection of oneself is God because it varies always. And then, He realized that his understanding was incomplete.

Seeking clarity, he returned to Praja:pathi. He stayed for 120 years more in the gurukula and perceived real truth.

Examining the eyes of a patient, doctor diagnoizes whether the patient is living or not. This means that eyes indicate if there is life in the body. Thus, eyes are the gateways of life. In fact, God supports that life. So, eyes are the place of God now.

Indra realized this truth and became very humble. He started respecting everybody for he saw God in the eyes of every creature. He became a de:vatha.

Moral - Don't take hasty decisions. Be patient. Learn good things.

Project

1. Create a poster on

    1. asura qualities and de:vatha qualities.

    2. good student and bad student

2. Draw eyes of different creatures.

I. Group Project

Perform Puppet Show on the story of Bramha losing Ve:das and regaining the lost Ve:das.

1. Create an audio CD. It must contain the sounds of fighting, Lord appearing from fire etc. Use it as the soundtrack.

2. Write a script for the puppet show.

3. Then create either string puppets or sock puppets.

    Perform your puppet show on the dais. Make it a ticketed show 50 cents, 1 $ etc. Donate the amount to local VT Seva coordinator to use it for educating underpriviledged.

II.   Research

Bramha is the creator. He creates all beings using Ve:dic knowledge he received from Lord Hayagri:va. Great scientists are also similar to Bramha as they created TV, light, rocket, cell phone etc.

List 10 inventors and their contributions to the society.

III.   Did you know?

Bramha is only 51 years old according to his time. Let us see how.

1 human year	=	1 day and 1 night for de:vathas
360 days and nights of de:vathas	=	1 de:vatha year
12,000 de:vatha years	=	1 Chathuryuga (4,320,000 human years)
71 Chathuryugas	=	1 Manvantharam (life span of one Manu)
14 Manvantharas	=	1 kalpa (1 day of Bramha)
2 Kalpas	=	1 day + 1 night for Bramha
360 days of Bramha	=	one year to Bramha
100 Bramha years	=	life span of one Brahma

Now, can you calculate age of Bramha in human years?

Slo:ka 9

I. Choose the right answer

1. _____ is the guru of de:vathas.
   - a. Sukra:cha:rya
   - b. Bhrugu
   - c. Bruhaspathi
   - d. Indra

2. De:vathas have a stable government because of
   - a. their sincere effort
   - b. their intelligence
   - c. able direction of their a:cha:rya
   - d. the proper leadership of Indra

3. Lord Hayagri:va gifted Bruhaspathi with
   - a. wealth
   - b. determination
   - c. sathva guna
   - d. rajo: guna

4. The king of de:vathas is
   - a. Indra
   - b. Va:yu
   - c. Agni
   - d. Varuna

II. Fill in the blanks with Sanskrit words

1. Bruhaspathi's advice made the _____ of de:vathas stable.

2. Lord eradicated the _____ of Bruhaspathi.

3. Lord blessed Bruhaspathi with _____guna: .

III. Answer the following

1. What are we praying for in this slo:ka?

2. Explain the picture for this slo:ka in your own words.

3. What happens if you have wavering thoughts?

4. When can one overcome the wavering and unstable thoughts?

IV. Solve the puzzle with Sanskrit words for the clues given below

Across

4. empire

Down

1. untouched

2. then

3. guru of de:vathas

5. as

V. Unscramble

HYAHATA ☐☐☐☐☐☐☐

HIRT ☐☐☐☐

AASD ☐☐☐☐

DET:NA ☐☐☐ : ☐☐

VAE ☐☐☐

LO:DA:M ☐☐ : ☐☐ : ☐

VI.   Complete the picture

Imagine you are meditating on Lord Hayagri:va. All your wavering and unstable are being driven out and good thoughts are occupying your mind. Name them. For example – see picture of sloka 5

VII. Maze

Can you help Bruhaspathi receive the grace of Lord Hayagri:va.

IV. Learn More

Kids	-	Jai Srimannarayana Grandpa!
Grandpa	-	Jai Srimannarayana Kids.
Vishnu	-	What does sathva guna mean?
Go:da	-	Don't you know? We learnt it in Module 2.
Vishnu	-	Hmm.. I faintly remember…. Can you tell me grandpa?
Grandpa	-	Sure.. listen.. There are 3 gunas – sathva guna, rajo: guna and thamo: guna
Vishnu	-	What does guna mean Grandpa?
Grandpa	-	Guna is an attribute.
Vishnu	-	Who has these gunas?
Grandpa	-	Nature has these 3 gunas. They influence all the objects, living and non-living.
Go:da:	-	oh! Then, we too have them?
Grandpa	-	Yes. Our bodies are products of Nature only. Hence, our bodies too have these 3 gunas.
Goda	-	Can we see these gunas?
Grandpa	-	No, they are not visible. But they are exhibited through our words, deeds, attire and the surroundings we organize.
Vishnu	-	So… gunas influence our behavior. Right Grandpa?
Grandpa	-	Not only ours Vishnu. They influence the other creatures too. Gunas provoke our actions.
Goda	-	In what way Grandpa?
Grandpa	-	A person with rajo:guna is in an agitated mood, irritating others with rough behavior etc.,
		A person with sathva guna speaks good words, acts well, dresses plain, leads a simple life and is helpful.

Goda	-	Do we have control over these gunas?
Grandpa	-	Fortunately, only we, human beings have this capacity. But, we need to make an effort to improve sa:thvik quality in us.
Vishnu	-	But, how can we control these 3 gunas, I mean how can we become more sa:thvik?
Grandpa	-	Let any quality dominate in us, but by practice we can control unwanted quality and enhance sa:thvik guna.
Vishnu	-	Can you give us an example grandpa?
Grandpa	-	Sugri:va was a ra:jasik but he turned sa:thvik by joining Ra:ma and serving him. So also Vibhi:shana, a tha:masik by birth yet surrenderance to Ra:ma helped him in enhancing sathva guna. Whichever guna is predominant in a person, practice enables him to become sa:thvik.

Now go and revise your Module 2 book and tell me about rajo:guna and thamo: guna.

Kids	-	Sure Grandpa. Thank you. Jai Srimannarayana.
Grandpa	-	Jai Srimannarayana

V. Classify to which gunas the below belong

Meat, milk, stealing, coke, selfishness, waking up late, grapes, drumstick, knife, picture of Krushna, blue color, scenary, stale food, poster showing violence, red big stripes dress, neat reading table, alcohol, white color, onions, violent movie, coffee, anger, plain dress, laziness, hurting someone, garlic, bar, envy, ego, volunteering, cursing, reading good books, gentle, deceit, kicking, sleeping late, messy room

VI. Group Project

Let 3 – 4 students form a group and create a presentation. The presentation should be less than 10 minutes.

Indra had Bruhaspathi as his guru. Bhrushaspathi was a sa:thvik sage and

he guided Indra properly. Hence, Indra is able to rule his kingdom properly.

1. How can a sa:thvik leader influence people?

2. What happens if the leaders are ra:jasik or tha:masik? Who will be affected?

3. What do you recommend to the present leaders?

4. Examples of sa:thvik, ra:jasik and tha:masik rulers from ancient or modern history. Lessons to be learnt from those examples.

VII. Did you know?

* Right from birth to death, man undergoes many physical changes. But de:vathas are always 30 years old during their lifespan.

* Many think that there are 330 million de:vathas i.e 33 crores of de:vathas.

However, in Sanskrit, 'Ko:ti' means a division, a wing or 10 millions. Hence, there may be 330 million de:vathas as per the definition. But, using the other meaning, it means that there are 33 wings or divisions among all the de:vathas.

Ve:das and other scriptures mentioned the names of these 33 divisions. They are-

* 12 A:dithyas to support the life of all creatures in the Universe.

* 11 Rudras responsible for changing the phases of Universe for better recycling

* 8 Ashta Vasus for nurturing the Universe

* 2 Aswini De:vathas take care of medical and health departments

Slo:ka 10

I. Choose the correct answer

1. In yajnas, priest puts offerings in the
    - a. pot
    - b. well
    - c. sand
    - d. holy fire

2. Oblations in yajnas are offered by
    - a. chanting names
    - b. singing songs
    - c. reciting ve:dic manthras
    - d. all of the above

3. _____ receive energy from the sacrificial offerings.
    - a. Asuras
    - b. De:vathas
    - c. Priests
    - d. Scholars

4. Ve:dic manthras get the energy
    - a. as they are in sanskrit
    - b. as they are recited by trained scholars
    - c. as they are sung musically
    - d. as Lord is the indweller

5. De:vathas relish the offerings when
    - a. samidhas are dry
    - b. ho:ma kunda is big
    - c. relevant manthras are recited
    - d. none of the above

II.   Correct the spellings

1.   Athastivan

2.   Samdha:rchisi

3.   Havishom

4.   Akandasarih

5.   Apyayanam

III.   Fill in the blanks with Sanskrit words

1.   Lord! You have _____ (manthra mayam, havisha:m) _____
     (**sari:ram**, akhanda) _____(a:thastthiva:n, agnou)

2.   Lord, you permit _____(a:pya:yanam, sari:ram) to the
     de:vathas.

3.   The oblations are filled with _____(akhanda sa:rahihi, agni)

IV.   Answer the following

1.   How do we offer oblations to de:vathas?

     _____

     _____

2.   Explain the picture of the slo:ka.

     _____

     _____

3.   How are Ve:dic hymns energized?

     _____

     _____

V. Do you remember?

In Module 2, you learnt how a ho:ma kunda looks like and also the materials
used to perform yajna. List the names of materials used in the yajna.

VI. Coloring corner

Ho:ma kunda can be constructed in different shapes depending on the type of yajna one is performing. Below are the sketches of a few fire altars. Draw the missing items in those altars and color them.

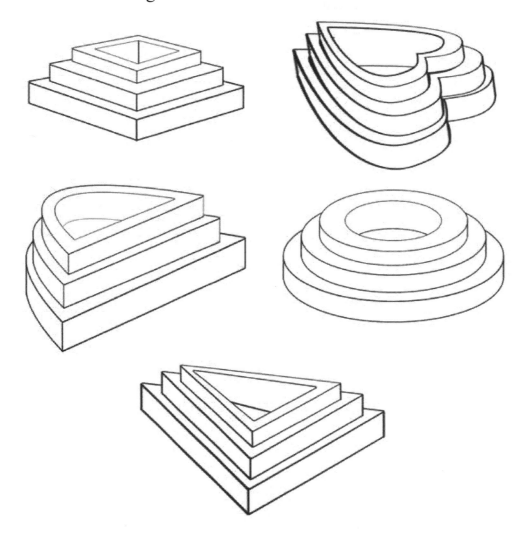

VII. Solve the puzzle using Sanskrit words for the clues given below

Across

4. in the fire

6. you permit

7. made of manthras

Down

1. by delivering

2. oblations

3. blazing flames

5. divine body

VIII. Learn More

Grandpa	-	Good Evening kids!
Kids	-	Good evening grandpa. What did you do today?
Grandpa	-	Well, I did meditation on Ashta:kshari manthra today.
Go:da	-	What is a manthra Grandpa?
Vishnu	-	I heard that word many times but don't know what it really means!
Grandpa	-	Manthra is defined as "mantha:ram thra:yathe: ithi manthraha" Manthra is one which protects whoever chants it with faith.
Go:da	-	Protection from what, grandpa?
Grandpa	-	We always are in need of something everytime. Also, new troubles crop up every now and then. Manthra helps in overcoming those hurdles. Thus we can fulfill our desires and wishes. A manthra forms a protective shield around us.
Go:da	-	hmmm.. But, how are God and manthras connected? I mean – what is …
Grandpa	-	I understood your question. It is the manthra which creates the channel between us and God and thus makes us experience him. Our scriptures symbolize manthra as a Mother.
Vishnu	-	Wow! Let me pick up a small manthra from Ve:das and chant it from today.
Grandpa	-	No, that is not the way. You need to get manthra from a qualified guru. Hence, our scriptures say that A:cha:rya is our Spiritual Father.
Goda	-	Are there any other rules Grandpa?

Grandpa	-	Chanting manthra will be effective and powerful if you get it from a qualified guru. Also, it should be chanted properly. Evena small mistake will make it ineffective. Not only that, it will cause disturbance in the Nature around us. Hence, manthrasneed to be learned under a qualified guru with rapt attention and faith. Sometimes wrong chanting of manthra wil lead to ill health. Therefore,chanting with proper intonation and accent is important
Vishnu	-	Can you tell what is intonation and accent?
Grandpa	-	Yes but not now. Now off you go and do your homework.
Kids	–	Jai Srimannarayana Grandpa.

IX.   Did you know?

There are forces in Nature. Any movement in our body or around us is only because of these forces. These forces are called de:vathas. We need to attribute all activities as services to de:vathas. De:vathas help us and we serve them in return. Lord Krushna instructed us to do yajnas to serve the de:vathas.

How can we do yajna?

Every activity we do should be attributed to de:vathas. Then, that act will be transformed as yajna. Lord Krushna in Chapter 3 of Bhagavad Gi:tha said -

de:va:n bha:vayatha:ne:na

the: de:va: bha:vayanthu vaha |

parasparam bha:vayanthaha

sre:yah param ava:psyattha || Slo:ka 11

man performs yajnas Help each other and prosper. De:vathas receive offerings

Slo:ka 6 – 10 Cumulative Exercises

I. Analogy

1. Siva is to Dakshina Mu:rthy :: Va:gde:vi is to
   _____

2. Bramha is to Saraswathi :: Siva is to _____

3. Rajo: guna is to aggressiveness :: sathva guna is to _____

4. Siva is to small drum :: Saraswathi is to _____

5. Hayagri:va is to Madhu, Kaitabha :: _____ is to Ra:vana, Kumbhakarna.

6. Sage Ve:da Vya:sa is to Para:sara :: Bramha is to
   _____

7. Sukra:cha:rya is to rajo: guna :: Bruhaspathi is to
   _____

8. De:vathas is to heaven :: demons is to
   _____

9. Bramha is to Siva :: _____ is to Gane:sa.

10. Rajo:guna is to red as sathva guna is to _____.

II. Odd Man Out

1. Dakshina Mu:rthy, Saraswathi, Ve:da Vya:sa, Hayagri:va

2. Saraswathi, Pa:rvathi, Durga, Ka:li

3. Ve:da Vya:sa, Va:lmi:ki, Suka Maharshi, Na:rada, Hayagri:va

4. Bruhaspathi, Indra, Va:yu, Agni, Varuna

5. Sukra:cha:rya, Bruhaspathi, Va:mana, Viswa:mithra, Gargi

6. Madhu, Kaitabha, Hiranyakasipu, Bhi:shma, Ra:vana

7. Siva, Dakshina Mu:rthy, Bramha, Trine:thra, Rudra

8. Fire, paper, ghee, wood, sruk, sravam

III. Match the words with their meanings

1.	Saro:ja	–	(a)	lotus
2.	Girisaha	–	(b)	Siva
3.	Va:gde:vi	–	(c)	saraswathi
4.	Daithya	–	(d)	demon
5.	Vya:sa	–	(e)	_____
6.	Bha:gade:yaha	–	(f)	wealth
7.	Thridase:swara	–	(g)	devathas
8.	Agni	–	(h)	fire
9.	Sari:ram	_	(i)	divine body
10.	Havisha:m	–	(j)	offerings
11.	Virinchaha	–	(k)	bramha
12.	Nigama:n	–	(l)	Ve:das

Subhashitham- A Moral

yada: kinchijno:ham dwipa iva mada:ndhas samabhavam

thada: sarvajno:smi: thy abhavad avaliptham mama manaha|

yada:kinchith kinchid budhajana saka:sa:th avagatham

thada: mu:rkho:smi ithi jwara iva mado: me: vyapagathaha ||

This couplet was written by Bharthruhari which speaks about the vanity that comes from half knowledge. When one has little knowledge, he is blinded with pride. He sees a larger than life portrait of himself. His behavior is similar to that of an arrogant elephant which disobeys his own master and wanders off. But once he associates with wise, he realizes his own deficiencies and slowly turns humble. Knowledge is like an ocean. Hundreds of years are not enough to learn it in full. This truth will be realized by a real seeker as a result of his association with learned.

Slo:ka 11

I. Choose the right answer

   1. O:M is originated from

      a.   O

      b.   U

      c.   A

      d.   M

   2. The whole universe consists of

      a.   sentient beings

      b.   non sentient beings

      c.   a & b

      d.   None of the above

   3. _____ is the Indicator of Supreme.

      a.   Bramha

      b.   'Uka:ra'

      c.   'Aka:ra'

      d.   'ma:ka:ra'

II.   True or False

1.   The divine syllable 'A' is the cause of all literature.

2.   Lord and divine syllable 'A' are inseparable.

3.   All objects originated from 'A'.

4.   Prame:yam and Prama:nam are the same.

5.   The divine sound is the combination of 'O' and 'M'.

6.   All the objects merge in the Lord.

7.   Finally the divine letter merges with the Lord.

8.   The whole Ve:dic literature is prame:yam.

9.   Sages realized the Lord as the meaning for 'A'.

10.   Lord is 'ksharam'.

11.   Divine syllable 'A' is 'aksharam'.

12.   Prama:**n**am tells of prame:yas.

13.   'Aka:ra' came from O:M.

14.   Aka:ra tells about Lord.

15.   Lord and 'Aka:ra' are called 'akshara ma:thruka'.

III.   Give the Sanskrit words for the following

1.   eternal letter

2.   wise

3.   eternal trees

4.   realizing

5.   origin

6.   source

IV.   Choose the right word and fill in the blanks

1.   The enlightened-souls _____(ja:nanthi, mu:lam) that _____ (o:m, aksharam) denotes you as the Supreme.

2.   The letter 'A' is the _____ (thathvam, mu:lam) for the _____ (a:mna:ya maha:druma:**n**a:m, aksharama:thruka:m)

3.   The entire world _____ (prathibha:thi, ya:) like this

V. Answer the following

1.   What is meant by 'akshara ma:thruka'?

2.   What is 'prame:yam'?

3.   What is 'prama:**n**am'. What does it determine?

4.   Classify the objects that can be perceived.

5.   How can you establish the Lord and the syllable 'A' as the 'Indicated' and the 'Indicator'?

VI. Solve the puzzle using Sanskrit words for the clues given below

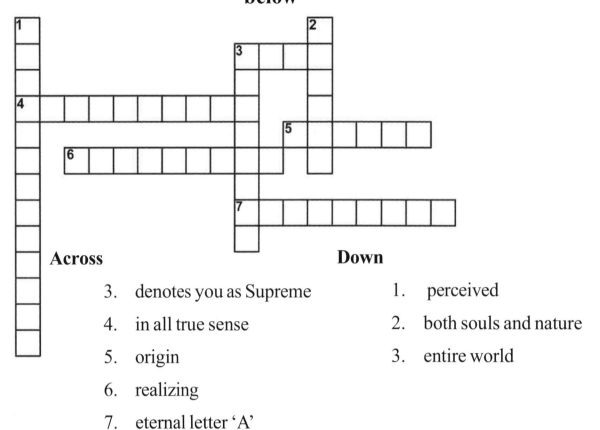

Across

3. denotes you as Supreme
4. in all true sense
5. origin
6. realizing
7. eternal letter 'A'

Down

1. perceived
2. both souls and nature
3. entire world

VII. Unscramble

I:KURD   ☐ : ☐☐☐☐

HAT:M   ☐☐☐ : ☐

TEH: ☐☐☐ :

UM:MLA   ☐☐ : ☐☐☐

AY: ☐☐ :

HYAT   ☐☐☐☐

VIII.Complete the diagram

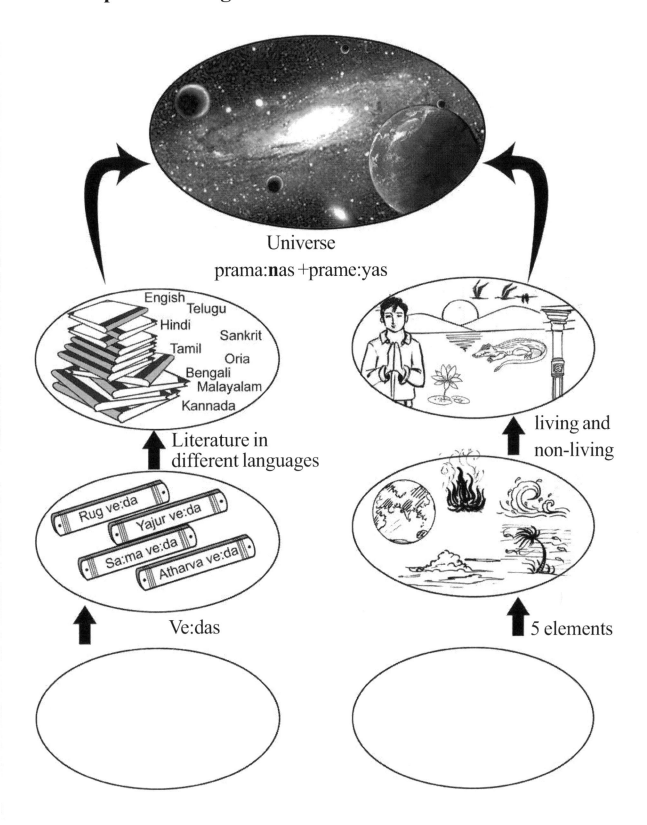

Universe
prama:**n**as +prame:yas

Literature in
different languages

living and
non-living

Ve:das

5 elements

IX. Sort Prame:yas and Prama:nas and place them in appropriate baskets

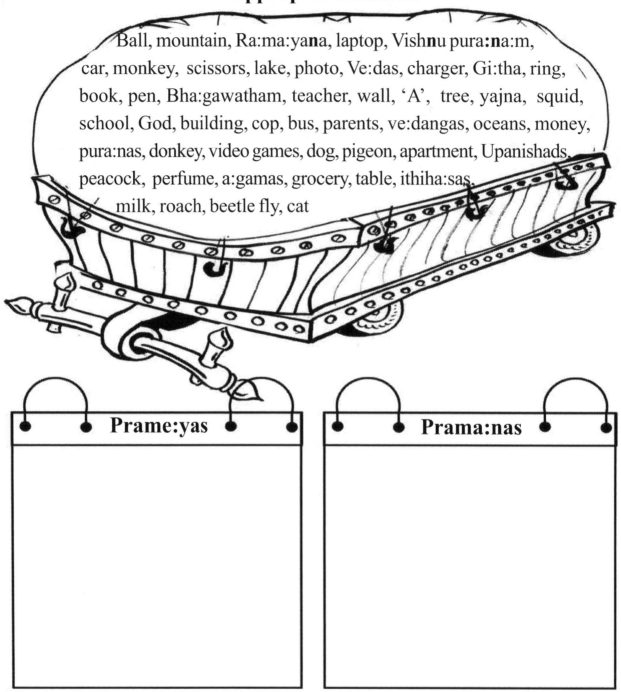

Ball, mountain, Ra:ma:yana, laptop, Vishnu pura:na:m, car, monkey, scissors, lake, photo, Ve:das, charger, Gi:tha, ring, book, pen, Bha:gawatham, teacher, wall, 'A', tree, yajna, squid, school, God, building, cop, bus, parents, ve:dangas, oceans, money, pura:nas, donkey, video games, dog, pigeon, apartment, Upanishads, peacock, perfume, a:gamas, grocery, table, ithiha:sas, milk, roach, beetle fly, cat

Prame:yas

Prama:nas

X. Project

Draw a picture of God with O:M in the background. Make an attractive wal hanging. Give it as a gift to your friends.

Slo:ka 12

I. Choose the correct answer

1. In this state, objects have no name or form
    a. avya:krutha
    b. vya:krutha
    c. na:ma:ni
    d. none of the above

2. Lord protects the objects during
    a. creation
    b. sustenance
    c. deluge
    d. all the above

3. During deluge, all the objects remain in _____ form.
    a. macro
    b. same
    c. micro
    d. all the above

4. In the state of 'avya:krutha' objects are
    a. visible
    b. invisible
    c. clear
    d. none of the above

5. In the state of 'vya:krutha' objects are
    a. imaginary
    b. disgusting
    c. visible
    d. invisible

6. Objects go through avya:krutha or vya:krutha state due to
    a. will of Lord
    b. fantasy of Lord
    c. dream of Lord
    d. all the above

7. The supreme truth is revealed
    a. in Nature
    b. by scholars
    c. by singers
    d. in Ve:das

8. The supreme truth is realized by
    a. old people
    b. sages
    c. students
    d. None of the above

9. The plant which exists inside the seed is
    a. avya:krutha
    b. vya:krutha
    c. visible form
    d. none of the above

II.   Fill in the missing letters

1. R ___ ___ p ___ _____ N I
2. N ___ ___ M ___ ____ NI
3. Y ____ ___ N ____
4. ____ A M S ____ ____ T H ____
5. ____ H A ____ A M ____ M

III. True or False

1. Objects change in avya:krutha stage.

2. In vya:krutha state, new objects are created.

3. In avya:krutha dasa, every object cannot be perceived.

4. In vya:krutha dasa, objects cannot be seen.

5. Every object has a particular form and name.

6. Lord outstretches Himself as objects with name, shape and characteristics.

7. When Lord wills, He keeps everything in a minute/micro form in Himself.

8. At His own will, He draws out everything giving the objects a macro/visible form.

9. Seers got enlightened reading stories.

10. We can see a plant inside the seed.

IV. Write Sanskrit words for the following

1. Earlier

2. Realizing

3. Ultimate

4. Lord Hayagri:va

5. initial knowledge (upajna)

V. Complete the following with the Sanskrit terms from the slo:ka

1. The enlightened sages _____(samsanthi, pu:rvam) that Lord is the ultimate _____ (prathishtta:, ru:pa:ni).

2. Lord has outstretched Himself as objects with names and _____ (ru:pa:ni, na:ma:ni)

3. Earlier, the objects were in _____ (avya:krutha, charamam) state.

VI. Answer the following

1. How was the Universe in the beginning?

2. What did the Lord do at the time of creation?

3. Why is there no change in the forms or names on recreation?

4. What is avya:krutha dasa?

5. What is vya:krutha dasa?

VII. Unscramble

NUJPAA

HAHTTW

AY:NI

PU:RAMV

SIA

HAC

VIII. Solve the puzzle with Sanskrit words using the clues below

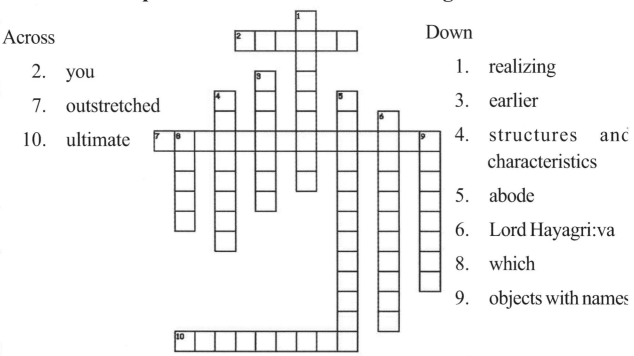

Across

  2. you

  7. outstretched

  10. ultimate

Down

  1. realizing

  3. earlier

  4. structures and characteristics

  5. abode

  6. Lord Hayagri:va

  8. which

  9. objects with names

IX. Do you remember?

1. In Module 2 you learnt that Lord creates, protects and dissolves the universe from this abode. Name the abode.

2. In which form does Lord create?

3. In which form does Lord protect?

4. In which form does Lord dissolve the world?

5. Name the stho:thra which talks about these three forms of Lord.

6. Quote the slo:ka which discusses about these three forms of Lord.

X. Learn More

In a tree, each part has a name. The whole tree takes a micro form in a seed.

In living objects it is little different.

In the case of a tree and seed, the tree gives seeds imprinting every detail in every seed.

And from the seed, colors, forms, shapes are recreated. But the names are unchanged. Seed, plant , tree, wood, coal, ash, earth. they form differer phases and go back. The states of the objects are prone to change. But eacl object has a phase and the name of that object in that phase is also fixed. Water, earth,

These elements take different shapes and again reach origin and in each shape the name is fixed.

But they keep changing from phase to phase.

XI. Workshop

Upanishads used several examples to make us understand the concepts o:
creation and dissolution. How do the below examples relate to the slo:ka
Explain it with illustrations.

1. Use play dough to make a tree or a flower. Re- knead it into a block to
    get back playdough.

2. Earth - Mud is used to make the pot. The pot when broken become:
    pieces and then mud again.

3. Water – Ocean water forms clouds. Cloulds bring rain. Rain water reache:
    the ocean.

4. Block of gold is used to make an ornament. The ornament when melte(
    becomes block of gold.

Can you come up with one example to explain the creation and dissolution:

Slo:ka 13

I. Choose the right answer

1. The showering moon light is
    a. cool and unpleasant
    b. cool and enchanting
    c. hot and beautiful
    d. none of the above

2. Lord Hayagri:va's form is the source of
    a. happiness
    b. nectar of bliss
    c. limited joy
    d. None of the above

3. The scholars _____ on the Lord's form.
    a. think
    b. meditate
    c. recollect
    d. None of the above

4. People who wish for _____ pray to Lord Hayagri:va.
    a. wealth
    b. eternal bliss
    c. good physique
    d. good health

5. Lord's magnificent form is like the enchanting shore of
    a. Pacific ocean
    b. Ganges
    c. Milky ocean
    d. Atlantic ocean

6. Scholars meditate on Lord's form
    a. in a temple
    b. at home
    c. in their hearts
    d. none of the above

II. Fill in the blanks with Sanskrit words from the slo:ka

1. Lord Hayagri:va's form is enchanting like the _____.
    (mugdhe:nduhu, sudha:prasu:thim)

2. The bliss is like ve:la: of the _____ (a:nanda, dugdha sindhuhu)

3. The scholars _____ (mu:rthihi, bha:vayanthe:) in their
    _____ (che:thas, a:nanda) the divine form of Lord.

III. True or False

1. Lord's magnificent from is enchanting.

2. The Milky Ocean is in North America.

3. The newmoon showers loads of moonlight.

4. The divine bliss is like the ocean tides.

5. Watching a fountain is a joy.

IV. Correct the spellings

1. dugda

2. rasitim

3. vilobaniyam

4. udaram

5. velam

V. Fill in the missing letters

1. A ___ N ___ ___ D ___

2. ___ U D ___ ___ :

3. MU___ ____ _____A

4. N ____ S ____ Y____ ____ _____ ____

5. V I ___ A ____ CH____ T ___ A ____ A

VI. Complete the slo:ka

_____ nishyanda _____

mu:rthim _____ sudha: _____

_____ che:thasi _____

ve:la:.m uda:ra:m _____

VII. Answer the following

1. What similies are used here?

2. How do the scholars feel while meditating on Lord?

3. Why is Lord's grace always compared to moon light and not sunlight?

VIII. Debate

Fountains are a waste of money and water.

IX. Give Sanskrit words for the following

1. Meditating

2. In the heart

3. Bliss

4. Divine form

X. Unscramble

HAATV ⬚⬚⬚⬚⬚

VIA ⬚⬚⬚

DIUN ⬚⬚⬚⬚

HDUAS ⬚⬚⬚⬚⬚ :

A:NADAN ⬚ : ⬚⬚⬚⬚⬚

XI. Solve the puzzle with Sanskrit words for the clues given below

Across

1. bewitching

3. scholars

4. nectar

6. divine bliss

Down

2. beautiful moon

3. shore

5. your

XII. Group Project

Create a model on one of the following

1. A Fountain. Challenge – Add light and music to your fountain.

2. Milky Ocean with white soft sands

3. Landscape on a full moon day

XIII. Research

1. In which scriptures do we find the mention of fountains?

2. List 10 incredibly beautiful fountains around the world.

Slo:ka 14

I. Choose the correct answer

1. Lord Hayagri:va moves like a _____ in the heart of a devotee.
   - a. royal swan
   - b. royal fish
   - c. tidal waves of an ocean
   - d. none of the above

2. Words are at the command of one who
   - a. has wealth
   - b. is sincere
   - c. has faith in Hayagri:va
   - d. none of the above

3. Chanting 14th slo:ka blesses one with
   - a. a good fortune
   - b. good personality
   - c. spontaneous speech skills
   - d. none of the above

4. One has to be _____ while praying to Lord.
   - a. sincere
   - b. playful
   - c. serious
   - d. none of the above

5. Indweller of our heart is
   - a. Swan
   - b. Lotus
   - c. Lord Hayagri:va
   - d. None of the above

II.   Give Sanskrit words

1.   Always

2.   On their own/ on his own

3.   Seeing

4.   To him

5.   Languages/words

6.   heart

7.   King

8.   Swan

III.   Correct the spellings

1.   tasya

2.   pasyati

3.   yatharham

4.   manishinam

5.   svayam

IV.   Complete the slo:ka

_____   _____ yassada: thwa:m

_____ ma:nasa ra:jahamsam

swayam _____

kurvathe: ___ _____

V. Fill in the missing letters

1.   M __ N ___ H ___

2.   P ____ ____ A ___ A

3. GI ___ ____ ____ A

4. B ____ A ____ J ____ ____ A

5. P ___ ____ Y __ ____ ____ I

VI. Answer the following

1. Who is a true devotee?

2. What is a devotee's heart compared to? Who stays there?

3. How does the Lord bless a devotee?

4. Under whose command are all the languages?

VII. Choose the correct words and fill in the blanks

1. Lord! You dwell in the _____ (manaha, thasya) of _____ (ma:nasa, mani:shina:m).

2. Devotees _____ (sada:, thasya) meditate on you.

3. You move like a _____ in the hearts of devotees. (ra:ja hamsa, giraha)

4. The languages _____ (kim kurvathe:, ma:nasa) to the devotees who meditate on Lord Hayagri:va.

5. The words of all languages are _____ (thasya, yattha:rham) serving the devotees.

VIII. Solve the puzzle with meanings of the clues given below

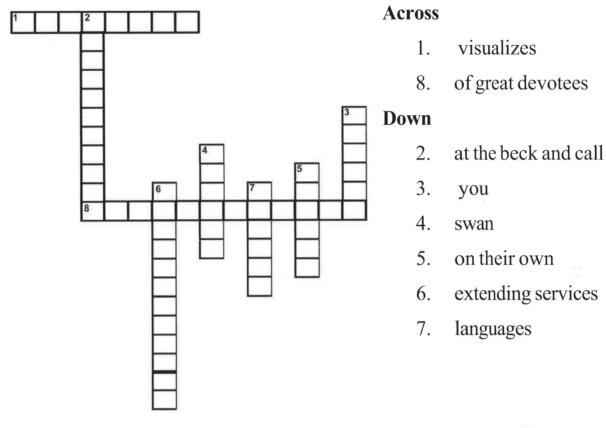

Across

1. visualizes
8. of great devotees

Down

2. at the beck and call
3. you
4. swan
5. on their own
6. extending services
7. languages

IX. Unscramble

DASA: ☐☐☐☐ :

AAHY ☐☐☐☐

RA:JA ☐☐ : ☐☐

TYHSAA ☐☐☐☐☐☐

GIAHRA ☐☐☐☐☐☐

X. Speak spontaneously on one of the below topics

Speak in front of the class for two minutes without pausing. Points will be cut for using 'ums' and 'uhs', and beginning sentences with 'so'. The speech must have a logical beginning and end.

1. Serve all beings as service to God.

2. Prayers improve our personality.

3. Prayer improves memory.

4. Prayers make us better citizens.

5. Living is the art of loving.

6. Loving is the art of sharing.

7. Sharing is the art of praying.

8. Praying is the art of living.

9. Worship your own, respect all.

10. Lord always protects us.

XI. Comprehension

Swans are beautiful, large and majestic water birds. They drink milk. While drinking milk, they leave the water behind. Milk is equated to good values and water with lesser values. Good people are considered as swans.

Both good and bad exist in this world. Good people can segregate good from bad and choose the good like the swan. When we take good people as role models, we will also be able to develop the ability to segregate between good and bad. Then, we will develop courage to accept only good things.

Swans also have some symbolism in our Vedic culture. A swan is called hamsa in Sanskrit. A:charyas are compared to hamsas and if the a:cha:ryas are superior, they are called 'Paramahamsas'. A:cha:ryas have two titles –

·   Paramahamsa - who is able to realize the difference between divine and worldly objects.

·   Parivra:jika - They go round the world to spread the message. Hence, they are called pari + vra:jaka a:cha:ryas – always on the move.

XII. Project

You are attending the local community fair. As you are a VT Seva coordinator, you are suddenly invited to the dias to speak about global warming and its effect on migratory birds. How would you organize your speech in your mind and speak spontaneously?

XIII. Research

1. Find words for the following in five different languages.

   a. Swan

   b. Lake

   c. Heart

   d. Mind

   e. Service

2. Find five famous lakes in the world.

3. Find three famous lakes in India.

XIV. Did you know?

❋   Bramha's vehicle is swan.

❋   Lord took the form of a swan.

❋   Swans used to live in Lake Ma:nasa saro:var in olden days.

SLO:KA 15

I. Choose the correct answer

1. Minimum time required to meditate
    a. fraction of a second
    b. one hour
    c. five minutes
    d. twenty four hours

2. The devotees of Hayagri:va get the eloquence which
    a. is slower than the flow of River Ganga
    b. is faster than the flow of River Ganga
    c. is equal to the flow of River Ganga
    d. none of the above

3. We should serve the lord
    a. with love
    b. with devotion
    c. with affection
    d. all of the above

4. Chant 15th slo:ka to speak
    a. realistically
    b. eloquently
    c. pleasantly
    d. convincingly

II. Choose the correct word and fill in the blanks

1. _____ (ye: \ thwa:m) pray to you even if _____ (kshana:rttham \ manda:kini:m) , _____ (the: \ thwa:m) will be blessed.

2. Devotees of Hayagri:va are blessed with perfect flow of _____ (mayu:khaihi \ va:cha:m).

3. With chaste _____ (**s**anaihi,mayu:khaihi) Hayagri:va
    _____ (a:pla:vayathi, kshamanthe:)

III. Correct the spellings

1. mandayutum

2. mandakinim

3. vacham

4. aplavayamthun

5. thvam

IV. Frame the slo:ka

1. manda:kini:m 2. va:cha:m 3. a:pla:vayantham 4. api 5. kalayanthi 6. thwa:m 7.mandayithum 8. aniva:rithais the: 9. mayu:khaihi 10. vi**s**adair

11. kshana:rttham 12. ye: 13. prava:hair 14. kshamanthe:

V. Fill in the missing letters

1. ani ___ ___ ___ r i _____ _____ a i hi

2. m __ y ___ ___ k ___ a ____ hi

3. pr ___ _____ a ___ ____ a _____ h ____

4. v _____ ___ a d ____ _____ hi

5. k ___ l ___ y ____ n ___ ____ i

VI. Questions

1. What similies are used in this slo:ka?

    To speak – have good communication skills and be able to give a powerful speech.

    Speaking abilities – create general questions

       Know your audience

Punch lines

Share a story

Focus on benefits

reiteration

self confidence

live and energetic

knowledgeable about the subject

look good, have stage presence

no stumbling, using good language

speak with conviction

connect with audience

logical flow

precise

well mannered

VII. Unscramble

HET ☐☐☐ :

EY: ☐☐ :

NAAKSH ☐☐☐☐☐☐

MTRATHA ☐☐☐☐☐☐☐

PIA ☐☐☐

VA:ACH:M ☐☐ : ☐☐☐ : ☐

VIII. Solve the puzzle with equivalent Sanskrit words for the clues given below

Across

2. of communication

6. affectionately serve

Down

1. with chaste

3. flow of River Ganga

4. even for a split second

5. rays of grace

IX. Research

1. Five famous personalities known for their eloquence.

2. Origin of River Ganga

3. Name of the River Ganga at its origin.

   Find out from which place the river acquired the name Ganga

Slo:ka 11–15 Cumulative Exercises

I. Analogy

1. Prame:yas is to all perceivable objects :: pramanas is to
   _____

2. Akshara is to indestructible :: ma:thruka is to _____

3. _____ is to an 'Indicator' :: divine syllable _____ is to 'Indicated'

4. Trees is to prame:yas :: Upanishads is to _____

5. Lord is to objects :: 'a' is to _____

6. Avya:krutha is to invisible state :: _____ is to visible state.

7. 14ᵗʰ slo:ka is to fluent speech :: 15ᵗʰ slo:ka is to
   _____

8. De:vathas is to _____ :: Bha:gawatham is to Prama:nam.

9. Manda:kini:m is to river :: _____ is to swan.

10. 'a' is to first syllable of O:M :: _____ is the last syllable of O:M.

II. Odd man out

1. A, u, m, i

2. Prama:nam, prame:yam, pa:the:yam

3. Animals, birds, Gi:tha, human beings, de:vathas

4. Stars, moon, nectar, milky ocean, swan

5. Animals, birds, humans, trees, stones

6. Ganga, Bhagi:rathi, Ja:nhavi, Vishnupa:da, Ve:daha

7. Á', de:vathas, Supreme Lord

8. A:mna:yaha, Ve:daha, sruthihi, agnihi, thrayi:

III. Match the Following

1. mughdhe:ndu – full moon
2. sudha: - nectar
3. dugdha sindho:ho – milky ocean
4. che:thasi – in their hearts
5. manda:kini:m – ganga
6. ra:jahamsa – king of swans
7. giraha – languages
8. manishina:m – great devotees
9. aksharam – eternal letter 'a'
10. mu:rthihi – divine form

Footnote – *as* is denoted *::*

IV. Subhashita:ni

> ye:sha:m na vidya: na thapo na da:nam
>
> jna:nam na si:lam na guno: na dharmaha |
>
> the: marthyalo:ke: bhuvi bha:rabhu:tha:ha
>
> manushyaru:pe:na mruga:s charanthi ||

Those without learning, austerity, charity, knowledge, character, qualities and good practice are considered animals in human guise moving on the earth adding pain to her.

Slo:ka 16

I. Choose the correct answer

1. Meditation fills bliss
    a. in our hearts
    b. in each and every cell of our body
    c. in our mind
    d. none of the above

2. Joy experienced during meditation is
    a. a normal experience
    b. rare experience
    c. similar to going to Disney World
    d. similar to buying a new dress

II. Fill in the blanks with Sanskrit words

1. Lord! The blessed devotees are experiencing _____ (dhya:na, pulaka:nubandham).

2. The result of the bliss can be seen _____ (ange:shu, kwa:pi).

3. Devotees take shower in your _____ (dhya:na, bhavath) sudha: .

III. Give Sanskrit words for the following

1. somewhere

2. as though

3. meditation

4. blessed ones

IV. Correct the spellings

1. rakshanam

2. parivahanyanti

3. vardhamanam

4. amantam

5. dyana

V. Answer the following

1.   List the similies or metaphors used to explain the joy experienced by a devotee.

2.   How does our body react when in joy?

3.   How and from where does God shower his grace?

VI. Similes and Metaphors

Similies and metaphors are used to compare two different things in a descriptive manner.

A similie uses the word "like" or "as" to make the comparison.

A metaphor directly compares two things by saying that one actually is the other.

Examples of similes

I was standing perfectly still, like a statue.

I slept like a log.

She is beautiful like the moon.

Examples of Metaphors

Life is a roller coaster of emotions.

It is raining cats and dogs.

Identify similies and metaphors from the below sentences

1.   I'm as hungry as a tiger!

2.   I was a tiger attacking my food!

3.   Si:tha's voice is velvet.

4.   Aakash is as strong as a bull.

5.   Indu is like a human calculator.

6.   You are my hero.

7. The sun was a furnace.

8. Manisha slept like a log.

9. Swetha was as sweet as pie.

10. Srirag is lightning as he runs the race.

11. Sri is a fish when she swims.

12. Anurag is like a computer when he does his math.

13. The music was as soothing as rain.

14. Manish is as hungry as a horse.

15. He is a lion.

VI. Unscramble

WAK ⬜⬜⬜

AIP ⬜⬜⬜

AVI ⬜⬜⬜

DUHSA ⬜⬜⬜⬜⬜

MU:MAL ⬜⬜ : ⬜⬜⬜

VII. Solve the puzzle with meanings in English for the clues given below

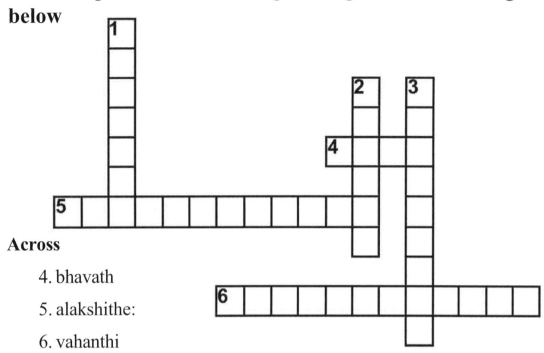

Across

    4. bhavath

    5. alakshithe:

    6. vahanthi

Down

    1. dhanya:ha

    2. abhishekam

    3. ankurantham

VIII. Workshop

In this slo:ka the devotees of Lord Hayagri:va experience 'goose bumps'.

1. What are goosebumps?

2. Who gets goosebumps?

3. When do we get goosebumps?

4. What are the other reactions in our body when we get goosebumps?

5. Where do you get goosebumps on your body?

6. Write some situations in which you experienced goosebumps.

7. Analyze Dhruva's reaction on seeing God.

IX. Learn More

Go:da	-	Grandpa! Grandpa!
Grandpa	-	Yes dear!
Go:da	-	In the Prajna class, we always come across the word 'bliss'. What does it mean?
Vishnu	-	Don't you know? Bliss means happiness.
Go:da	-	But why should we pray God to get happiness?
Vishnu	-	Yeah Grandpa! Why? We get joy doing many things like spending time with friends
Go:da	-	playing video games, going to movies, eating ice-cream etc
Grandpa	-	Good question. Now, you guys tell me how long does that happiness stay?
Go:da	-	Well! For some time.
Grandpa	-	What happens later?
Vishnu	-	Well…. we become normal.
Grandpa	-	, don't you think that this happiness is limited?
Vishnu	-	Yeah… it is limited.
Goda	-	Are happiness and bliss the same?
Vishnu	-	How can I always be happy?
Grandpa	-	One question at a time kids. Goda, Happiness and bliss are not the same. Pleasure is physical comfort. Happiness is a positive feel. Joy is good experience, a bit higher than happiness. Bliss is the divine experience greater than the joy.
Goda	-	How can I be in the state of bliss grandpa?
Grandpa	-	Well, only by the grace of God. Hence we pray God to bless us with eternal joy. It is the state of bliss or 'a:nanda'. It is one of His divine qualities.

| Vishnu | - | woow.. I wish I can enjoy that bliss. |
| Goda | - | Yes, me too. I will start praying God to grant me this joy. Thankyou grandpa for making us understand what real happiness is. |

Questions

1. What is bliss?

2. Site instances when you were happy and for how long.

3. In what **s**lo:kas from Hayagri:va Stho:thram did you encounter the word 'a:nanda'?

4. Project - Create chart to show the different states of joy with instances you experienced.

X.Learn more

In Sanskrit, a seed is called 'beeja'. When the seed starts sprouting it is called 'ankura'. 'Ankurantha' is the verbal form of the word 'ankura'.

Tree gives us many things. And, the tree comes from the seed. Thus, seed is the root cause of the tree. A seed when planted, sprouts. This sprout is the initial stage of the tree. The sprout, Ankura gives a hope and confidence to the farmer that it is going to yield wonderful results.

Similarly, when we have faith in God, the moment we remember God or the

beeja

ankura

Tree

thoughts of God give us peace and joy. These are like ankuras of the seed.

Knowledge is like a seed. When it is sowed in the water of God's qualities, it leads to ultimate bliss. And the first step is peace and joy. Thus, knowledge gives peace and joy. When it is slowly nurtured it will lead to bliss or a:nanda.

II.Project

You must be aware that in all the rituals performed in our homes or temples, they conduct an activity called 'ankura:rpana'.

1. Variety of seeds are soaked in milk and sowed in twelve clay plates. Make a research on this. Identify the names of seeds, types of clay pots and understand the procedure and relevance of it. Prepare a paper on it.

2. Make a Nature book. For each grain, find out its scientific name, its habitat, when it gives seeds, and other information. Make sure to draw a detailed picture of the plant, and its seed. Also attach a sample of the seeds in a plastic bag. Share with the class.

3. Make a dish using sprouts, and bring it to the class.

Slo:ka 17

I. Choose the correct answer

1. Overwhelmed joy brings
   a. tears
   b. laughter
   c. claps
   d. none of the above

2. High tides occur
   a. on new moon day
   b. on full moon day
   c. during eclipses only
   d. once in a month

3. Lord! bless us to
   a. experience joy
   b. eat well
   c. sleep well
   d. study well

4. _____ are always in Lord's view.
   a. Devotees
   b. Scholars
   c. Nature
   d. None of the above

5. One can become wise at heart as a result of _____.
   a. meditating on God
   b. travelling across the world
   c. doing yo:ga
   d. none of the above

II.   Fill in the blanks with Sanskrit words

1. Lord! Your devotees are _____ (dhanyaha, ama:ntham) prathicha hrudaye:na.

2. Devotees 'experience of joy is _____ (chandra, pariva:hayanthi) as tears.

3. Devotees experience _____ (dhya:na, a:nanda payo:dhim) by deep meditation.

III.   Correct the spellings

1. Puyobhi

2. Rakshanm

3. Chadrodaya

4. Hridayina

5. swamin

IV.   Complete the slo:ka

swa:min _____ _____ dhanya:ha

_____ dhya:na _____ vardhama:nam |

ama:ntham _____ _____ manthaha

_____ _____ pariva:hayanthi ||

V. Answer the following

1. What metaphors are used for joy and meditation? Explain them with reference to context.

2. What is the effect of moon rise on the waters?

VI.   Match the metaphors

1.   Life is a   apple of my eye

2.   Sun is a   gem

3. His eyes are   orange ball

4. You are a   journey

5. Time is   blossoming lotuses

6. He is a   giant

7. His heart is a   racing

8. She is the   peaceful home

9. I am drowning   is foggy

10. My memory   in studies

VII. Solve the puzzle with equivalent Sanskrit words for the clues given below

Across

    2. like the appearance

    4. within them

    6. irrepressible

Down

    1. through the waters

    3. of moon

    4. in their eyes

    5. by deep meditation

VIII. Learn More

Kids   -   Grandpa, can we ask you a question if you don't feel embarrassed?

Grandpa -   Yeah, ask! But don't expect answers.

Kids   -   Why did you cry when you were praying to God today?

Grandpa	-	Oh, it happens sometimes, when I go into deep meditation.
Vishnu	-	Oh, I know, in Hayagri:va Stho:thram, I read that when one is in deep meditation, joy overflows from the heart in the form of tears.
Goda	-	A few people even get goose bumps!
Grandpa	-	Not only that, great saints and devotees experience the li:las of the Lord and laugh, cry, or even faint! In fact, they feel the presence of the Lord. They forget the time and place they are in and react to the situation as if it is happening in front of their eyes.
Goda	-	Is there anyone like that Grandpa?
Grandpa	-	Ofcourse there are a lot. Mi:rabai, Thya:gara:ja, Ra:mdas, Kabir, Annamaya, Saint Namma:lva:r, the list goes on….. All their songs are results of their experiences. Mentally they were in that scene. When we listen to those songs, we also feel that we are in those situations.
Goda	-	Yes grandpa, I heard a beautiful song describing how Lord Krushna stole butter, Mother tied him to the pestle and Krushna cried. Isn't it so grandpa?
Grandpa	-	Yes, Krushna was tied up to the pestle and was crying. Thinking of that incident, saints like Nammalva:r fell unconscious for 6 months.
Kids	-	Wow.
Grandpa	-	Kids, go and present Krushna's incident using a diorama.
Kids	-	Sure Grandpa. Jai Srimannarayana.

X. Workshop

Meditation

❈   contemplating on any object, living or non-living

* visualizing the form, size, shape, color, activities and any possible qualities

* trying to establish a relationship with that

* feeling deep love on that, not able to get separated from it

* trying to actualize in due course of time

* To do all the above, arranging a calm and quiet space, creating a serene atmosphere around.

Now, choose Lord Hayagri:va as your focus.

Try to sit and meditate in your Prajna class.

1. How long could you sit and meditate?

2. In what posture did you sit to meditate?

3. Did you meditate by closing your eyes or opening your eyes?

4. Did you get any other thoughts while meditating?

5. Did you feel like moving your hands, legs or open your eyes while meditating? How did you control it?

6. How do you feel after meditation?

7. How does meditation help?

X.Research

Did you know, according to scientific studies, on full moon day, seeds germinate faster and plants grow at a faster rate.

Moon is called 'so:ma' in Sanskrit. Our Ve:das give a lot of importance to Moon. Moon is considered as the Lord of all the plants. It is the cause for plants to grow, and provide us with healthy food grains.

1. What effect does the Moon have on the ocean?

2. How does Moon influence plants?

3. Can moon influence human behavior?

4.   Identify the mentioning of moon in our past prayers.

XI.   Did you know?

1.   Our tears have different temperatures and taste differently depending on our emotions. Typically, tears that fall from our eyes in pain, sorrow, guilt, etc are warm and salty. However, tears that roll down with love for God or in happiness and joy are cool and non-saline.

2.   Did you know, we all have swimming pools in our eyes!

What are the parts of a swimming pool? We need something that generates the water, something that stores the water, and something that drains it!

Similarly, in our eyes, a tissue called the lacrimal gland generates the fluid. This gland is next to the outer and upper corner of each eye.

Once the water is created, it flows downwards into an area called the conjunctival sac. It is present behind the eyelids.

When you jump into a swimming pool, what happens? Water splashes out! This is what exactly happens when you cry.

When you cry, the sac pushes the water out. When the eyes are filled, water rolls down the cheecks. The extra water drains out into the nose, through a pipe called the nasolacrimal duct. That's why your nose starts running when you cry a lot. Pretty cool, right?

Picture of an eye – c

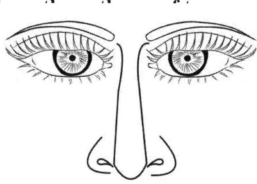

Slo:ka 18

I. Choose the correct answer

1. Nature is like a
    a. colorful rainbow
    b. hypnotic wand
    c. walking stick
    d. none of the above

2. _____ is Lord's favorite place too!
    a. World
    b. Disney World
    c. Sea World
    d. Dream World

3. Nature is under the control of
    a. wise men
    b. devotees
    c. God
    d. None of the above

4. _____ attribute their powers and thoughts to Lord.
    a. Wise men
    b. Dull heads
    c. Egoistic people
    d. None of the above

II. Fill in the blanks with Sanskrit words

1. The mysterious Nature is like a _____ .

2. _____ are able to surpass the mysterious Nature.

3. This inert world is also Lord's _____ .

4. Devotees have Your _____

5. The wise have dedicated _____ towards You.

III. Unscramble

1. mo:hana the: vaiha:riki:m pinchhika:m

2. thwadanu samruddhavi:rya:s grahe:**na**

3. na:ttha! ma:ya:m vipaschitho: tharanthi

4. bha:va:s bha:va:ha thwadadhi:na swaira:nu

IV. Answer the following

1. How can one surpass the mysterious Nature?

2. Why is Nature called 'ma:ya:'?

3. What do wise men do?

4. What are we praying for in this slo:ka?

V. Here are five indriyas. Unscramble them

SINK

NOES

AER

YEE

NOTGEU

VI. Learn More

Goda   -   Grandpa! Grandpa! Can you please explain this picture?

Grandpa   -   Sure, let me see it.

Grandpa   -   It is a ferris wheel with some labels on it. Can you guys club

them into groups?

Goda	-	Eyes, ear, nose, tongue and skin are five sense organs of our body.
Vishnu	-	Eyes enable us to see, ear to hear, nose to smell, tongue to taste and skin to feel.
Goda	-	These enable us to enjoy the world around us.
Grandpa	-	Correct. These sense organs always make us focus on the world around us and consume everything as food.
Goda	-	Food? But how can our eyes or ears eat food grandpa?
Grandpa	-	Everything we see around us is the food for sight. What ever we breathe is food for nose. Whatever we taste is the food for tongue and so on. Now, Vishnu what is the next group you can come up with?
Vishnu	-	sa:thva, rajas and thamas.
Goda	-	These three are the gunas
Goda	-	The other group is manas - mind, buddhi - intellect and ahanka:ra - ego
Vishnu	-	These three are like drivers. They control our sense organs and make us behave in a certain way.
Grandpa	-	Very good children, what is the next group?
Goda	-	Grandpa , what are pa:da, pa:yu and Pa:ni?
Grandfather	-	These are mortar organs called ' karme:ndriya:s'. Infact we have 5 motor organs. va:k – tongue to speak, pa:ni - hands, pa:da - feet, Pa:yu – anus and upastha - urinary tract.
Goda	-	And, what are ka:ma, kro:dha,lo:bha, mada, moha, ma:thsarya?
Grandfather	-	These are the six instincts of the mind causing sorrow or joy. These six instincts together have a technical term in Sanskrit.

Vishnu	-	What is it grandpa?
Grandpa	-	"arishad varga"
Vishnu	-	What do they mean?
Grandpa	-	'Ka:ma' means lust, 'kro:dha' means anger, ' lo:bha' means greed, 'mo:ha' means unwarranted attachment, 'mada' means pride and 'ma:thsarya' means jelousy and envy.
Vishnu	-	But, why are all these labeled on a ferris wheel grandpa?
Grandpa	-	We, Ve:dics believe in rebirths. We, the souls are stuck in this ferris wheel of birth and death and cycle of sorrow. We are ignoring the Lord and are unable to enjoy the bliss. One should come out of the negative impact of the arishad vargam.

Then his ego - ahanka:ra comes under control. Joy and sorrow will be neutralized.

Then the five sensory organs will be tamed towards us.

Sathva will be increased. Rajas and thamas go down. Mind – manas becomes peaceful and then the buddhi gains sa:thvik energy.

A person with such wisdom will be able to enjoy the warmth of His grace.

Goda	-	Grandpa, If buddhi – wisdom becomes sa:thvik then mind becomes peaceful right?
Vishnu	-	Then manas – mind also becomes sathvik and is peaceful. Rajas and thamas will no longer be aggrevated . Correct?
Grandpa	-	Yes.
Goda	-	Then sensory organs too will listen to us and will not get agitated.
Vishnu	-	Comforts or discomforts will not lead to joy or sorrow.
Goda	-	Though we come across circumstances that provoke arishad

vargas, we will not become their victim. Right grandpa?

Grandpa - Wow.. kids you are awesome!

Questions

1. What are the six insticts called?

2. What are the three gunas?

3. How many sense organs do we have? What are they?

4. Why are we stuck in this gaint ferris wheel?

5. How can we get rid of the vices?

6. You are fasting as it is Eka:dasi. You are volunteering in a Food Fair event and are surrounded by yummy foods.

 a. What sense organs get activated?

 b. What is your reaction?

 c. What can you do to increase your will power and continue to fast?

VII. Complete the puzzle with the 6 instincts we have using Sanskrit words

Across

 5. jealousy

 6. anger

Down

 1. greed

 2. unwarranted attachment

 3. lust

 4. pride

4. jealousy

VIII. Project

Prepare the model of ferris wheel. Find the biggest ferris wheels in the world and label your model after that.

IX. Comprehension

In a certain town, there lived a farmer named Haridattha. He was very poor.

One day, while Haridattha was resting under the shade of a tree, a cobra emerged from an anthill and confronted him with its raised hood. Haridattha thought to himself, "Perhaps this cobra is the form of God staying in my farm. Let me worship it from today." As if the cobra heard the farmer, it immediately disappeared into the anthill.

Haridattha placed a plate with milk near the anthill, offered prayers and then, left for home. Next morning, he came to the farm and was astonished to see a gold coin lying on the plate. Haridattha's joy knew no bounds. Everyday, he made an offering of milk to the cobra and the cobra gifted him with a gold coin.

One day, Haridattha had to visit the nearby village. He instructed his son to offer milk to the cobra. Accordingly, on the following day, his son did so and then went home. When the son came back the next morning to offer prayers, he was surprised to see a gold coin lying on the plate.

He thought to himself, 'This anthill must be full of gold coins. I'll kill the cobra and get all the gold at once.' He hid himself behind the tree after placing the plate of milk near the anthill. The snake came out as usual to

drink the milk. Haridattha's son attacked it with a stick. But, luckily for the cobra, it was not a death blow. The angry cobra bit Haridattha's son and went away. The boy died on the spot.

Questions

1. Why did Haridattha offer milk to the cobra?

2. Haridattha's son inherited the qualities of his father. Do you agree?

3. Suggest a title for this story.

4. Which one among the arishad vargas is highlighted in this story?

5. What is the moral of the story?

Slo:ka 19

I. Choose the correct answer

1. Chintha:mani is
   - a.   name of a girl
   - b.   a gem
   - c.   a mountain
   - d.   a river

2. Eternal bliss can be attained by
   - a.   riches
   - b.   gems
   - c.   penances
   - d.   prostrations

3. _____ are carried forward from previous life.
   - a.   Sins
   - b.   Clothes
   - c.   Genes
   - d.   None of the above

4. _____ are like real riches.
   - a.   Chintha:mani
   - b.   Penances
   - c.   Lotus feet
   - d.   Prostrations to Lord

5. _____ is the most divine gem.
   - a.   Kausthuba gem
   - b.   Diamonds
   - c.   Sri:vathsa
   - d.   Chintha:mani

II. Fill in the blanks with Sanskrit words

1. This divine _____ (chintha:ma**n**i, pra:k) gem fulfills the desires.

2. Let the prostration of mine lead me towards your _____ (pa:da padma, pra**n**a:ma:ha)

3. I offer _____ (pra**n**a:maha, pa:da) which lead to _____ (ni**ss**reyasa, sampadaha).

4. Let my services _____ (nirmitha:na:m, same:dhishi:ram) at Your lotus feet.

III. Complete the slo:ka

pra:ng _____ thapasa:m _____

_____ _____ sampado: me: |

same:dhishi:rams _____ _____

_____ chintha:ma**n**ayah _____ ||

IV. Correct the spellings

1. pranamaha

2. chinthamanayah

3. nisreyasa

4. samkalpa

5. preetyagra

V. Answer the following

1. What is the result of our past penances?

2. What should our goal of life be?

3. What can fulfill all our desires?

4.   What are prayers compared to?

5.   What is the specialty of gem 'chintha:mani'?

VI.   Learn More

Go:da	–	What is prostration?
Vishnu	–	It means bowing down. Right Grandpa ?
Grandpa	–	Yes, it means bowing down.
Goda	-	Before whom?
Grandpa	-	Before parents, elders, gurus and God out of reverence and submission.
Goda	–	When should we postrate Grandpa?
Vishnu	–	Did we not learn in Module 1? We have to prostrate before mother everyday in the morning.
Grandpa	–	Correct. We prostrate before parents, gurus, elders and God in the morning. We seek special blessings from them on occasions such as birthdays, festivals, important days and when we are about to start a new task.

Pranipa:tha:na si:lasya nithyam vruddho:pase:vinaha |

Chathwa:rasthasya vardhanthe: ayur vidya: yaso: balaha ||

Who ever prostrates before elders will be blessed with longevity, knowledge, fame and strength.

Kids	–	Wow!
Grandpa	–	As per our scriptures one should also prostrate before wise irrespective of their age. No matter what a person's status is in the society, whether he is the president or a peasant, he should prostrate to a:cha:rya.
Goda	–	How do we prostrate?
Vishnu	–	Are there any rules?

Grandpa	–	Yes… we should touch the ground with 8 parts of our body – 2 hands, 2 feet, head, manas - mind, buddhi – intellect, and abhima:nam – ego. It is called *ashta:nga prana:ma.*
Vishnu	–	Today we learnt what is *ashta:nga prana:ma.*
Goda	-	We will share it with our friends. Thanks Grandpa. Jai Srimannarayana

Questions

1. Find out how one prostrates in these religions.

    a.   Baha'i Faith

    b.   Buddhism

    c.   Christianity

    d.   Islam

    e.   Jainism

    f.   Judaism

    g.   Sikhism

2. To whom and when should one offer prostrations?

3. Draw a picture of girls and boys prostrating before a:cha:rya.

4. Do you think namaska:ram is also a prostration? Justify.

5. Do you think Lord Ra:ma and Lord Krushna prostrated before anyone?

VII. Unscramble

HVTAA [ ][ ][ ][ ][ ]

AP:DA [ ][ ] : [ ][ ]

PAR:K [ ][ ][ ] : [ ]

ME: [ ][ ] :

PDEMA: [ ][ ][ ][ ][ ] :

VIII. Solve the puzzle with English or Sanskrit meanings for the clues given below

Across

4. which are like riches

6. leading towards bliss

Down

1. progress

2. prostrations

3. at the lotus feet

5. in the past life

IX. Research on one of the topics as a group of 3-4 and present in the Prajna Parents Meet

1.   Types of gems

2.   Where are they found?

3.   Their influence on us

4.   Birthstones and gems – are they the same?

5.   Rebirth

X. Did you know?

Ve:das revealed many details about rebirth. Souls are permanent. Nature is also permanent. Nature forms bodies of different species. Though Nature is permanent, the formed bodies are temporary. Soul takes a body to consume some amount of karma. The moment allotted karma is consumed, soul leaves that particular body. It takes another body for experiencing some other karma.

Slo:ka 20

I. Choose the correct answer

    1. All the devotees adorn _____ on their heads.
- a. crowns
- b. flowers
- c. divine dust of Lord's feet
- d. turbans

    2. _____ erases the evil fate.
- a. Holy dust
- b. Sun
- c. Eraser
- d. None of the above

II.   Fill in the blanks with Sanskrit words

1. Let there be _____ (bhu:ya:n, bhu:yath) grace of

   _____

   (viluptha, thvadanghri ra:ji:va rajah kana:nam)

2. I bow to the feet of Lord which _____
(sure:ndra chu:dapada lalitha:na:m, viluptha mu:rdhanya la:litha:nam) *(both options are correct)*

3. I am always indebted to those feet because _____ (
bhu:ya:n, viluptha mu:rdhanya lipikrama:na:m)

III.   Fill in letters to complete the words

1. L ___ P ___
2. S U __ __ ___ N D ___ ___
3. ___ A Y ___ :
4. BH __ ___ Y __ ___ N
5. BHU ___ ___ ___ : TH

IV. Unscramble

1. thvadanghri ka**n**a:na:m rajah ra:ji:va

2. prasa:do: na:ttha bhu:ya:n mayi bhu:ya:th

3. chu:da:pada la:litha:na:m sure:ndra

4. mu:rdhanya karma:**n**a:m viluptha lipi

V. Answer the following

1. What is considered holy and why?

2. What is fate?

3. Can we change fate?

4. Explain the benefits of adorning our heads with the holy dust?

VI. Debate

1. Good activities always give good results.

2. Conquer the fate.

VII. Solve the puzzle with equivalent English/Sanskrit words for clues given below.

Across

2. raji:va anghri lipi

4. bhu:ya:n

5. prasa:daha

6. on me

Down

1 which erase vipulptham

3. Indra

VIII. Maze

Mohan is trying to get rid of evil fate. Can you help him?

IX.   Learn More

Go:da	–	No! Evil fate means karma.
Vishnu	–	You are wrong. Karma means action.
Go:da	–	No, I am not wrong. Karma means…
Grandpa	–	Kids! What are you arguing about?
Kids	–	Grandpa! What is karma?
Grandpa	–	Karma means action. It also means the stock of records of past deeds.
Vishnu	–	Mmm….. Still not clear grandpa!
Grandpa	–	Vishnu! Strike a key on this laptop.
Grandpa	–	What's happening?
Vishnu	–	Well, it is showing up something….
Goda	–	Yeah, there is always an outcome when you strike a key.
Grandpa	–	Some are major, some are minor. Right?
Kids	–	Yeah!
Grandpa	–	Similarly, any action in the body yields some result.
Kids	–	Where?
Grandpa	–	Sometimes the result is limited to body; sometimes it expands to the Nature.
Goda	–	How?
Grandpa	–	For example, you say something, it goes into the Nature. It has an effect but it cannot be seen.
Kids	–	Do any actions show their effect on Nature?
Kids	–	Why not? If a nuclear bomb explodes, it breaches the ozone layer.
Goda	–	Oh yeah!

Grandpa	–	Did you guys observe that though Computer is not responsible for any action, all actions are recorded in it.
Vishnu	–	Oh yes! They are stored in the computer files.
Goda	–	One who has computer knowledge will be able to deal with them.
Grandpa	–	Similarly, body also maintains the records of all the actions done with it.
Vishnu	–	But, earlier you said that we cross through many bodies.
Grandpa	–	That is true, the records of all those bodies are carried by the soul.
Goda	–	My god, .. are all the records stored with me.
Vishnu	–	Is it so Grandpa? Am I carrying all the records?
Grandpa	–	Yes, you are carrying them.
Vishnu	–	Where are they?
Grandpa	–	They are preserved at various levels - at body level, senses, mind, intellect. With every body, new records are created and some old records are deleted.
Goda	–	How is it possible Grandpa?
Grandpa	–	Why not? The memory power in each of the cells on our body is unbelievably many many terra bytes.
Goda	–	When will these records be deleted?
Grandpa	–	When the soul leaves, people burn the body. Records at body level will be burnt, but records at other levels will be well preserved. Only grace of God can delete them.
Vishnu	–	Oh is it 'viluptha' in the sloka?
Goda	–	The sloka says that it will take care of records on heads. What about others?

Grandpa	–	Actually, it symbolically implies all records that exist at othe levels.
Kids	–	Oh!
Grandmother	–	Dinner is ready.
Grandpa	–	Lets go kids.

X. Research

1. Find out names of 10 de:vathas.

2. Find out different types of information storage systems

      ❀   in ancient times

      ❀   modern age

Slo:ka 16-20 Cumulative Exercises

I. Odd man Out

1. swa:min, na:ttha, va:gi:swara, hayavadana, ase:sha

2. Ear, tongue, eye, hands, nose, skin

3. ka:ma, manas, kro:dha, lo:bha, mo:ha, mada

4. Love, devotion, bhakthi, surrender, compassion

5. Lotus like feet, lotus like hair, lotus like eyes, lotus like hands

II.　Match the following

1.	abhishe:ka:th	–	taking shower
2.	akshanam	–	eyes
3.	dhyana	–	meditation
4.	chandra	–	moon
5.	payo:bhihi	–	through the waters
6.	pa:dapadme:	–	lotus feet
7.	sampadaha	–	riches
8.	chinta:mani	–	divine gems
9.	prana:maha	–	prostrations
10.	sure:ndra	–	indra
11.	mu:rdhanya	–	from our heads
12.	ankura:na:m	–	sprouting

SLOKA 21

I. Choose the correct answer

1. The divine feet resemble _____ flowers.
   a. tulip
   b. lotus
   c. mums
   d. jasmine

2. Ignorance is eradicated
   a. by Lord's glowing anklets
   b. by sunrise
   c. by lotus flowers
   d. by studying

3. Anklets dazzle like
   a. Sun
   b. Moon
   c. Stars
   d. Planets

4. The heart of a devotee blossoms with _____.
   a. lotus flower
   b. knowledge
   c. sound of anklets
   d. none of the above

II. Correct the spellings

1. prabudha

2. nirduta

3. nupur

4. vibata

5. antaha

III. Reframe the slo:ka

1. parichinmahe: 2. the: 3. sandhya:m 4. parka:sa 5. chithrabha:nu 6. nu:pura 7.anushanga:m 8. vibha:tha 9. anthaha 10. ra:ji:va 11. parisphurath 12. thamaha 13. nirdhu:tha 14. prabo:dha 15. pada 16. dwayi:m

IV. Fill in the missing letters

1. dwa___ ___ ____ _____

2. ni___ d ____ ____ : ____ ha

3. c___ i ____ ____ r a ____ ____ a ____ n u

4. s ___ ____ d h ___ a : ____

5. a ___ u ____ ____ a ____ ____ a ____ m

V. Who am I?

1. I eradicate the ill fate of my devotees.

2. Even de:vathas and kings yearn to have me on their chu:da:ngam.

3. The rising sun enables me to blossom.

4. I shine like thousands of suns.

5. I adorn Lord's divine feet.

6. The radiance of Lord's lotus feet eradicates me.

VI. Answer the following

1. How is our ignorance eradicated?

2. List the similies and their usage in this prayer.

3. What makes our hearts bloom with knowledge?

VII. Complete the blanks to form similes.

I am as ....

1. lazy as _____
2. cold as _____
3. loud as _____
4. big as _____
5. busy as _____
6. small as _____
7. strong as _____
8. fair as _____
9. tall as _____
10. gentle as _____
11. brave as _____
12. hot as _____
13. slow as _____
14. fast as _____
15. light as _____
16. heavy as _____
17. fat as _____
18. thin as _____
19. beautiful/smart as _____
20. intelligent as _____

VIII. Draw

1. Beautiful anklets for Lord Hayagri:va.

2. Rising sun

3. Lotus

4. Butterfly hovering on the lotus

IX. Use the words and make a story

lotus, water, crocodile, lord , his disc, eagle, elephant

X.. Project

1. List the ornaments decorated to God. Make them and label them.

2. Make an Origami Lotus flower. Demonstrate the steps in front of the class.

XI. Research

1. Different shades of sun during sun rise and sunsets.

2. Name the flowers that bloom at sunrise.

3. Name the flowers that bloom at sunset.

4. Find out the different phases in a day and the difference in the sun rays.

5. Why is feet compared to a lotus?

6. Synonyms of sun in Sanskrit.

Sloka 22

I. Choose the correct answer

1. Devotees adorn _____ of Lord on their heads.
    - a. anklet bells
    - b. Ve:das
    - c. divine fish
    - d. lotus feet

2. Your anklets have a _____ sound.
    - a. joyous
    - b. divine
    - c. melodious
    - d. all of the above

3. Lord's incarnation as a fish is called
    - a. Mathsya:vatha:ra
    - b. Hamsa:vatha:ra
    - c. Ku:rma:vatha:ra
    - d. Vara:ha:vatha:ra

4. Lord recovered Ve:das in this avatha:ra
    - a. Sri:Rama
    - b. Sri:Krushna
    - c. Hamsa:vatha:ra
    - d. Va:mana

5. _____ are the caskets of Ve:das.
    - a. Anklets
    - b. Crown
    - c. Feet
    - d. None of the above

II.   Fill in the blanks with Sanskrit words

1. The _____ of yours is the casket of Holy Ve:das.(mani nu:puram,

2. Ve:das were _____by Lord in other eras too.(pa:litha:h,

3. We are meditators of _____ (ve:dagira:m,) which are thwat _____ Alankara_____

III.   Fill in the missing letters

1. Ki __ k __ r ___

2. Ma___ ____ ____ : s ____ i ____ a _____ m

3. K ___ l ___ a

4. Ve: ___ ____ g i ____ _____ ____m

5. P r ___ t ____ i _____ m a ____ a

IV.   Reframe the slo:ka

1. prathi:maha 2. pa:litha:na:m 3. mani nu:puram 4. thvaya: 5. kinkara 6. thwath 7. the: 8. ve:dagira:m 9. kalpa:nthara 10. manju:shika:m 11. manju 12. prana:dam 1. e:va 14. uchitha:na:m 15. alankarana

V. Answer the following

1. Describe the anklets of Lord Hayagri:va?

2. What is the store house of Ve:das and since when?

3. How many avatharas did Lord take to recover Ve:das?

VI. Unscramble

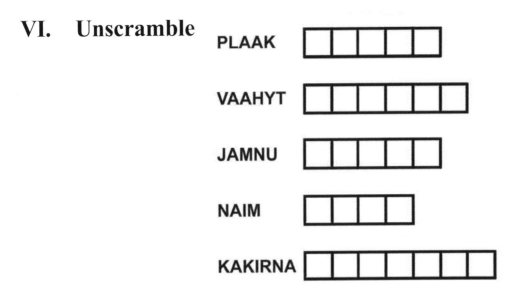

PLAAK

VAAHYT

JAMNU

NAIM

KAKIRNA

VII. Wordsearch

Below are 10 avathars of Lord Vishnu. Find them.

P V C A U S Q K Z E U E M Q V

S X D K M A F X R S C I O A H

E Y G P M R F A A U A S M A H

S R C A M G U H A N S A M X M

I P R E G T M K M G N H H Q O

F T M H M I A Z A A L G N Y N

X X D X S J E U R R C V I A I

V J F A V E R H U M L W V S K

L Z R J A N X C S X U U N H L

Q A H F R Z T X A X O W X Z A

N F O F A E R G R C V B L P K

E P I W H D T I A X A K M L X

R I G T A O Q O P G C E S Q Q

R E V M Z S V S V W K D K Q V

M A T H S Y A W L K G P K F Y

VIII. Do you remember?

Nu:puram means anklets. This word is used in Sri Krushna:stakam. Recollect that slo:ka while finding out the who decorates them and when.

IX. Workshop

Create a skit on Mathsya:vatha:ra and enact it in Prajna get-together.

X. Project

Make anklets with beads making a jingling sound and gift them to your mom, sister, or friend.

Sloka 23

I. Choose the right answer

1. Our hearts are like _____
   a. pots
   b. wicks
   c. earthen lamps
   d. none of the above

2. Our innovative knowledge is the result of _____
   a. our effort
   b. our study
   c. your blessings
   d. our intelligence

3. Wishfulfilling tree is the
   a. Kalpa vruksha
   b. banyan tree
   c. jasmine creeper
   d. rose shrubs

4. Lord preaching in jna:na mudra awards
   a. only knowledge
   b. only wishes and needs
   c. needs and salvation
   d. none of the above

5. Doctrines are like the
   a. lamp
   b. wick
   c. oil
   d. light

II. Fill in the blanks with Sanskrit words

1. Your _____ (madhuram karam, vijna:na) is in preaching seal.

2. Your hand glows like the pallava of vijna:na kalpa tree. (vya:khya:na mudra, kalpadruma pallava:bham)

3. _____ (samaya, sanchinthaya:mi) are like the bright light emitted by lamp of knowledge.

III. Fill in the blanks

1. Our hearts are like _____.

2. The knowledge is the _____.

3. Doctrines are the _____ emitted from the lamp.

4. Oil in the lamp should be _____ and _____.

5. Lord's affectionate blessing is the _____ in the lamp.

6. The glow of the light i.e knowledge is like the tender sprouts of _____

7. Eternal tree of knowledge is _____

8. Meditate on this slo:ka to develop great _____ power.

9. Lord blesses us with His _____ hand using Interpretative sign or mudra: .

10. We meditate on the _____ of the lord.

IV. Correct the spellings

1. a:bhm

2. palava

3. sthan

4. patiba

5. korum

V. Answer the following

1. How did the poet symbolize the heart and knowledge?

2. List the similies used in this prayer.

3. List the similarities and differences between Kalpa Vruksha and Lord's divine hand.

4. How do you relate the picture with the slo:ka?

VI. Word Search

```
K  A  L  P  A  D  R  U  M  A  Y  D  K  E  K
F  I  S  S  B  R  P  C  S  K  O  J  V  M  C
S  P  N  O  A  R  F  U  M  C  B  I  G  A  I
F  R  P  N  E  M  O  M  T  Y  T  T  S  R  W
A  I  E  A  O  N  A  R  K  A  V  E  U  U  F
R  R  C  D  I  V  I  Y  T  R  W  P  C  H  Q
H  H  D  M  N  N  A  E  A  O  L  R  C  D  E
V  P  U  U  E  E  R  T  M  Y  H  A  O  A  B
Y  L  K  S  M  P  G  T  I  Q  N  T  R  M  C
R  C  M  A  R  A  K  N  R  V  C  H  E  C  I
K  U  G  E  M  M  E  K  E  H  E  I  L  L  I
I  B  T  P  A  L  L  A  V  A  N  B  L  D  J
R  N  O  I  T  N  E  T  E  R  Z  H  X  H  M
I  E  P  O  Z  A  D  Z  B  A  W  A  X  A  E
N  V  P  L  N  Z  G  Y  A  H  J  U  E  D  Z
```

DOCTRINES	MUDRA
ENGENDERS	PALLAVA
INNOVATIVE	PRATHIBHA
INTERPRETATIVE	PREACH
KALPADRUMA	SAMAYA
KARAM	SUCCOR
LUMINOUS	RETENTION
MADHURAM	WICK

VII. Unscramble

RAMAK

SAAMAY

TEH: :

DARUM

ASDA: :

VAALAPL

VIII. Draw

Visualize the eternal tree of knowledge and draw it. What would its roots, branches, leaves be?

IX. Learn More

Grandpa is lighting a lamp in front of God.

Kids	–	Jai Srimannarayana Grandpa! Why are you lighting a lamp?
Go:da	–	Instead of an oil lamp, why don't you use an electric or a battery lamp?
Vishnu	–	Yeah? Why use oil, wick, container, etc, and take all that trouble?
Grandpa	–	You guys are always full of questions! Our elders asked us to practice certain things, and we have to do them without any question.
Vishnu	–	But Grandpa! There must be some logic behind.
Goda	–	Please tell us Grandpa.. – for own welfare
Vishnu	–	Can you enlighten me about two points
Grandpa	–	What are they During the day, we have enough light. Then is it necessary to have a lamp. In night, when there is enough light, why are you lighting a lamp in the mandir?
Grandpa	–	I would like to tell you two points – need of light and why oil and wick. Let me ask you a question first. Imagine you are in a giant pitch-black room. There is no light anywhere. You are surrounded by darkness. You are trying to find a pen in that room. Can you find it?
Go:da	–	No...
Grandpa	-	Now, imagine that you have a candle with you. You light it. What happens?

Vishnu	–	The whole room is illuminated.
Goda	–	We can now find not only the pen, but also many other things.
Grandpa	–	So, what do you conclude?
Vishnu	–	Well, its simple! In darkness, we can't see anything. When there is light, we can see everything.
Go:da	–	So, light removes darkness.
Grandpa	–	Our sages have compared jna:na with a lamp. Jna:na means knowledge, and ajna:na means ignorance. Ignorance is always compared to darkness. To remove the darkness, we must light the lamp of knowledge.
Go:da	–	Oh... But you can use any lamp! Why do you only use an oil lamp?
Grandpa	–	What do we need to light an oil lamp?
Vishnu	–	We need a container of some kind.
Go:da	–	We need some oil, wick and fire.
Grandpa	–	Exactly. Each of these symbolizes several aspects of gaining knowledge. One saint named Poighai A:lwa:r imagined the entire Earth as an earthen lamp, the oceans as oil, and the sun as the light. He used this lamp to gain the Ultimate Knowledge, that is seeing the Supreme Lord.

Vishnu & Go:da - Woooooooww

| Grandpa | – | Another saint named Pu:daththa used his love for God as a container, passion as the ghee, and his mind as the wick to light the lamp of knowledge. |

Vishnu & Go:da -   Amazing!

| Grandpa | – | Not only that, lighting oil or ghee lamps is considered to be auspicious. By lighting the lamp, we pray to God to remove the ignorance from our lives and fill our lives with the divine knowledge, jna:na. |

| Go:da | – | That's wonderful Grandpa, what a beautiful comparision. |
| Vishnu | – | From today, we too will light lamps before God! |

Questions

1. What is lamp compared to in the Hayagri:va sthothra?

2. Research how many wicks should be used to light a lamp before God.

X. Comprehension

Go:vinda Bhattar was a disciple of Bhagavad Ra:ma:nuja:cha:rya. Once he was asked to go to a dark room to do a few tasks. However, he was unsuccessful. When Bhagavad Ra:ma:nuja:cha:rya questioned as to why Go:vinda Bhattar failed to perform his tasks, he said, "When , You, my a:cha:rya are seated in my heart and are shining like a sun, I don't see any darkness anywhere!"

When there is Sun, there is no darkness. When we consider our A:cha:rya as the Sun, there will be no ignorance when we are in His presence. Hence, if we realize the greatness of our a:cha:rya as a jna:na bha:skara, the Sun of Knowledge, we can avoid darkness.

1. Why did Go:vinda Bhattar fail do to his task?

2. What does 'bha:skara' mean?

3. Suggest a title for this story.

4. Find out how many years ago this incident happened?

XI. Group Project

Form groups of four or five, and come up with a memory game based on Hayagri:va Stho:thram. Play this game in your class along with other Prajna classmates.

1. How did you come up with the idea for this game?

2. How long did you take?

3. What materials did you use?

4. For which age group did you make this game?

5. How long does this game take to play?

6. How did it bring out your memory skills?

7. What are your other observations?

XII. Memory Game

❋ Create cards with slo:ka pictures and label them

❋ Gather pictures of saints, a:cha:ryas, God in archa: form in divya desams and   famous temples ,God in different avathars and de:vathas.

❋ Glue them onto pieces of card. Label the pictures on the back of each of the cards.

❋ Try to remember each of the names. Mix up the cards and test yourself and your friends.

XIII. Research

1. List at least five different mudras and their benefits.

2. Story of the origin of Kalpavruksha

Sloka 24

I. Choose the correct answer

1. The chanting beads denote
   a. various branches of knowledge
   b. spirituality
   c. the irrigation wheel
   d. love towards devotee

2. Lord holds a _____ in His right hand.
   a. lotus
   b. garland of beads
   c. books
   d. thrisu:lam

3. Irrigation wheel is used in
   a. farms
   b. industries
   c. malls
   d. airports

4. The beads move like a/an
   a. irrigation wheel
   b. cart wheel
   c. top
   d. none of the above

5. Chant this slo:ka to obtain
   a. good memory power
   b. money
   c. health
   d. fame

6. _____ are used for irrigation purposes.

    a. canals

    b. wells

    c. irrigation wheels

    d. all of the above

II. Fill in the blanks with Sanskrit words

1. Lord! I meditate on your _____ (jna:na, savye:tharam karam) in my heart.

2. You are holding _____ (sphuritha:ksha, ghati:yanthram) beads in your right hand.

3. The garland of beads moves effortlessly like _____ (amrutha, ghati:yanthram).

4. Devotees meditate on the right hand to grab the _____ (karam, jna:na) amrutham.

III. Correct the spellings

1. lilasanum

2. asrithanam

3. aksamalum

4. thuadiyam

5. stitham

IV. Reframe the slo:ka

1. li:la: 2. jna:na 3. a:sritha:na:m 4. na:ttha 5. stthitham 6. savye:tharam 7. karam

1. karo:mi 9. sphuritha:ksha 10. chiththe: 11. thwadi:yam 12. la:lasa:na:m

2. ma:lam 10. amrutha 11. udanchana 12. ghati:yanthram 13. iva

V. Answer the following

1. Explain the similies used in this prayer.

2. What is the significance of beads in Lord's hands?

VI. Unscramble

RAAKM

SAAVY

HASKA

MA:MLA

VIA

LA:LI:

MAUHART

VII. Solve the puzzle with Sanskrit words for clues given below

Across

    3. grab

    6. which stays

    7. your

    8. irrigation wheel

Down

    1. shining

    2. Lord

    4. surrendered

    5. hand

VIII. Learn More

Vishnu	–	Why do you always wear that chain of beads around your neck Grandpa?
Goda	–	Yeah, only girls wear beads!
Grandpa	–	This isn't a normal chain, guys. It's called a thulasi ma:la.
Vishnu	–	Why are you wearing it?
Grandpa	–	Well, we all have a few inherent qualities in us. Some are good, and some are bad. To enhance our good qualities, we can use external sources. A thulasi ma:la is one such source which makes a huge difference in our thought process. It purifies our mind and improves our memory.
Goda	–	Oh, really? Can you give me one?
Vishnu	–	Uncle wears a different one. Is that a thulasi ma:la too?
Grandpa	–	No, it is made of lotus beads. Lotus flowers are very auspicious. They are the favorite flowers of Lakshmi De:vi. Also, a lotus signifies health, wealth, and prosperity. Hence, people wear ma:las made of lotus beads too.
Vishnu	–	So, can anyone wear these?
Grandpa	–	Yes, whoever wants to increase the above qualities can wear either of these.
Goda	–	Why do you use another ma:la for chanting?
Grandpa	–	That ma:la is called a japa ma:la. Some of us use it to keep a count of the manthra chanting. Each ma:la has 108 beads.
Goda	–	Are there any other types of ma:las?
Grandpa	–	Why not? Rudra:ksha ma:la, sphatika ma:la, etc. There are so many types!
Vishnu	–	Who uses them?

Grandpa	–	Why don't you guys find out and let me know?
Vishnu	–	We will! Do you have some more time Grandpa? I have another question.
Grandpa	–	Sure.
Vishnu	–	In this slo:ka picture, what is written on the chanting beads?
Grandpa	–	They are called Ve:da:ngas.
Go:da	–	What are Ve:dangas Grandpa?
Vishnu	–	I think Veda:ngas are Ve:das. Am I correct grandpa?
Grandpa	–	No. Listen carefully. Ve:das are complex, mystical and encrypted sounds. There are six auxiliary subjects which support Ve:das for better understanding. These six subjects are called Ve:da:ngas, meaning the 'limbs of Ve:das'.
Go:da and Vishnu	–	Thanks Grandpa. We will make flash cards with this information and show it to our Prajna teacher.

Questions

1. Who should wear the thulasi beads?

2. Find out the different varieties of the thulasi plant.

3. What do each of the beads – thulasi, lotus, sphatika, rudra:ksa look like? Draw pictures.

4. Gather samples of all four beads and display in your journal book.

5. What other religions use beads?

6. What are Ve:da:ngas?

7. How many Ve:da:ngas do we have?

IX.   Group Project

1.   Construct a model of an Irrigation Wheel.

2.   Collect pictures of different types of irrigation methods. Identify the ones which are environmentally friendly.

X. Memory Game

Play this game in your Prajna class.

The students will use the alphabets in Sanskrit and make words with them. They can use the words from the slo:kas they learnt so far.

Procedure:

The first student starts with the letter 'a' and says 'a' is for 'aksha'. Player 2 then repeats 'a' is for 'aksha' and then says 'a:'is for 'a:sritha:na:m'.

This continues through the alphabet until at Ha the last player needs to remember all the letters and the words attached to them from 'a' to 'ha'.

The winner is the first student to do it correctly.

XI.   Picture Puzzle

Ram is trying to make himself a chain with beads. These beads have different branches of knowledge inscribed on them. Being a sa:thvik boy, what beads will he pick ?

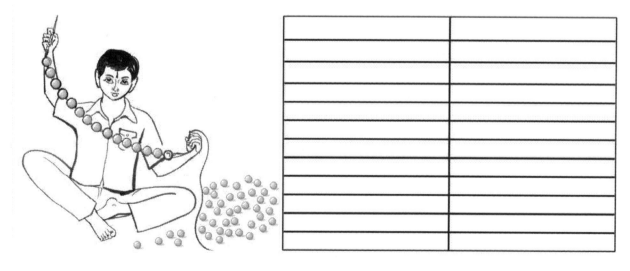

XII. Did you know?

Vedic Students' Memory

❋   In the olden days, students had immense concentration. They depended only on their aural skills. They never used any other resource to learn Ve:das. There was a specific method they employed.

❋   For each new lesson, the guru would spend ten days with the students. The next five days, the students would recite and memorize it. During the first ten days, the teacher would chant each verse once. Without looking at the book, the students listened to the verse and repeated it twice. At the end of 10 days, the students pretty much remembered the lesson.

❋   Then they would chant the new lesson they learnt from their guru ten times a day for the next five days. This is called oral tradition, Because they never referred to books, Ve:das became known as 'sruthi'. Meanwhile, their guru would begin a new lesson.

❋   Thus, Ve:dic students used to memorize each lesson by chanting it 100 times over 10 days, and remembered it throughout their life.

Sloka 25

I. Choose the correct answer

1. Lord holds _____ in His left hand.
   a. scriptures
   b. lotus
   c. chakra
   d. none of the above

2. Scriptures are compared to
   a. the ocean
   b. corals
   c. knowledge
   d. none of the above

3. In this slo:ka, we are worshipping the
   a. Lord's right hand
   b. Lord's left hand
   c. Lord's lotus feet
   d. none of the above

4. Corals are found in
   a. oceans
   b. rivers
   c. mines
   d. streams

II. Fill in the blanks with Sanskrit words

1. Lord! Your _____ (arunaihi, va:mam karam) shines with a rosy hue.

2. You hold a_____ (pusthakam, praka:saihi) in your left hand.

3. The scriptures shine like _____ (udwahantham, prava:la sangha:tham).

III. Answer the following

1. Describe Lord's hand.

2. What similies and metaphors are used in the slo:ka?

3. What should we wish for?

IV. Fill in the missing letters

1. de __ ___ ___

2. ud___ a ___ a ___ ____ ____ a ____

3. p r ___ b ___ ___ d h ____

4. s ___ n g ___ ___ : t ___ a ___

5. s ___ ___ i ___ ____ am

V. Correct the spellings

1. asritanam

2. hantum

3. vimam

4. sapushtakum

5. dukshinum

VI.   Learn Directions in Sanskrit (add pictures – HH)

Directions in Sanskrit are called 'disa:' or 'dik'.

Directions in English Directions in Sanskrit

East	pu:rva: dik/ pra:chi:
West	Paschima: dik/ prathi:chi:
North	Uththara: dik/ udi:chi:
South	Dakshina: dik / ava:chi:
North-east	I:sa:nya dik (i:sa:nyam)
South-east	A:gne:ya: dik
South-west	Nairuthi: dik
North-west	Va:yavya: dik
Up	U:rdhwa: dik
Down	Adhara: dik (adharam is lip, adhara: is corner)
Left	Va:ma: dik
Right	Dakshina: dik
Front	purastha:th, puraha
Back	Prusttaha

1. Make sentences using each of the above words.

2. Draw a map of your neighborhood. Identify at least one landmark in each direction.

VII. Word Search

```
S  S  H  S  K  U  A  C  O  P  Q
X  A  Z  F  P  D  W  V  M  Q  R
P  S  P  C  H  W  I  D  I  D  E
E  H  K  U  Z  A  B  C  A  B  A
E  L  J  O  S  N  M  K  Z  L  G
V  U  S  Y  P  T  S  K  M  S  E
A  W  I  I  Y  H  H  Y  O  H  F
D  J  E  U  I  A  T  A  R  A  J
B  V  M  N  I  M  I  E  K  L  V
D  M  A  H  T  I  H  T  S  A  X
D  M  M  E  A  G  V  B  U  V  M
```

DAKSHINAM

IVA

SAPUSTHAKAM

STHITHAM

UDWANTHAM

VIII. Unscramble

VA:AMM ☐☐ : ☐☐☐

RAMKA ☐☐☐☐☐

EHT: ☐☐☐ :

DE:AV ☐☐ : ☐☐

VAI ☐☐☐

IX. Comprehension

Sri: Para:sara Bhattar was a great a:cha:rya who lived in 12th century A.D. He was brilliant and very clever, even as a child. He was blessed with great knowledge and intelligence by Lord Ranganattha. We can understand his brilliance and ingenuity in the story below.

In the olden days, great scholars used to travel from one kingdom to another. They approached the rulers, exhibited their scholarship and sometimes challenged the local scholars for debates. In this process, rulers and the local scholars honored the guest scholars if they were worthy. They used to award the guest scholars with many accolades, precious gifts, lands, etc. To avoid defeat from the outsiders, the resident scholars always updated their knowledge frequently.

Once, a self-proclaimed scholar called Sarvajna Bhattaraka announced his arrival to Sri:rangam to debate with local scholars. He sent his disciples before him to project him in a grand way. He not only scared the scholars, but also insulted them. Scholarship should not make man arrogant. A scholar should always behave with humility and extend a helping hand to others. A real scholar shares his wealth of knowledge and uplifts others to his level.

Unfortunately, Bhatta:raka, was very arrogant and egotistical. The scholars of Sri:rangam were terrified of his impending visit. They were afraid of being defeated and ashamed publicly.

At that time, Sri: Para:sara Bhattar was only five years old. He observed the fear of his elders. He decided to protect the prestige of the Sri:rangam by retaliating against Bhatta:raka.

Sri: Para:sara Bhattar and his friends decided to meet the pundit while he was arriving by acting as if they were playing on the banks of the River Ka:ve:ri. The scholar was arriving in a palanquin. His entourage yelled at the playing children to get out of the way.

Bhattar asked, "Go around us. Why should we spoil our game?"

The palanquin bearers replied, "Silly boy. You are just a kid. He is a great scholar. Now move out of the way. "

"He is a scholar? What is his name? ", said Bhattar.

"He is Sarvajna Bhatta:raka" replied the bearers.

"Oh! What does it mean?" said Bhattar.

"It means that he knows everything. He is going to defeat the scholars in Sri:rangam.

Bhattar asked, "Really? Can I ask him small question?"

Meanwhile, Bhatta:raka observed the commotion from his palanquin. He called the boy to him.

Bhattar said, "Namaste, it seems you are all knowing person. I want to ask you a small question , if you don't mind.

The scholar laughed at him and said, "You are welcome to ask. "

Bhattar picked up a handful of sand from the ground, and asked, "See these sand grains? Can you say the count of this sand?

The scholar was dumbfounded. A few moments passed but no reply. His followers were irritated, but had no clue on what to say.

After a while, Para:sara Bhattar laughed at the scholar and said, " Can't you answer such a simple question. It is just a fistful of sand grains! What a great scholar you are! Oh Sarvajna Bhattaraka! You are going to defeat my teachers in this Sri:rangam," Para:sara Bhattar answered sarcastically. He ordered all his friends to stand in a line and showed the way into Srirangam.

The scholar not only felt insulted, but also scared to proceed into Srirangam. He thought, "If a young five year old boy is this intelligent, the great learned scholars of Sri:rangam must be much more formidable. If I couldn't even answer his question, how can I possibly answer theirs? It's best if I make a quick retreat before I embarrass myself and my reputation."

The prestige of Sri Rangam was saved because of young Para:sara Bhattar's intelligence.

1. Make a comic book for the above story.

2. Give a title for this story.

3. Name a few other child protégées.

X.Project

In ancient days, when there was no paper, our ancestors used palm leaves to make books. There was a special process to dry them. They used to engrave on the leaves with a sharp edge metallic pen. Even today, we can find these ancient books in our libraries.

Make a booklet resembling the palm leaf book.

Record the materials used.

Write the steps used to make this book.

Write the slo:kas you like the most in this book.

XI. Picture Puzzle

Help the diver find the gems in the ocean.

XII. Research

Find out about the scriptures of other religions.

Slo:ka 21 – 25 Cumulative Exercises

I. Analogy

1. Mruga mudra is to offer food to Lord :: jna:na mudra is to _____

2. Knowledge is to doctrines :: lamp is to _____

3. Kalpa vruksha is to fulfilling few needs :: Lord's Upade:sa mudra is to
   _____

4. Slo:ka 23 is to increasing retention power :: slo:ka 24 is to
   _____

5. Chanting beads is to bring out knowledge :: irrigation wheel is to
   _____

II. Odd Man Out

1. Plough, irrigation wheel, sickle, sword

2. Corals , lime stone, lord's hand, lotus

3. Power, oil lamp, sun, crystal, fire

4. Oil, ghee, wax, water, gas, wood, coal

5. Hamsa avatha:ra, mathsya avatha:ra, Hayagri:va, Ra:ma

6. Yo:ga, maths, law, cchandas, amrutha

III. Match the following

1.	raji:va	–	lotus
2.	nu:pura	–	anklet
3.	chitrabha:nu	–	like the sun
4.	padadwayam	–	feet
5.	manjushika:m	–	casket
6.	kalpadruma	–	kalpavruksha

7.	dasa:	–	wick
8.	vya:khyana mudra	–	preaching mudra
9.	akshama:la:m	–	garland of beads
10.	chiththe:	–	in my heart
11.	ghati:yanthram	–	irrigation wheel
12.	prava:la sangha:tham	–	cluster of rubies

Sloka 26

I. Choose the correct answer

1. Ignorance is compared to
   a. darkness
   b. light
   c. clouds
   d. moon

2. This bird's food is moonlight
   a. Cuckoo
   b. Nightingale
   c. Owl
   d. Chako:ra

3. Scholars are compared to
   a. moonlight
   b. chako:ra birds
   c. blooming lotus flower
   d. full moon

4. Lord is compared to
   a. lotus
   b. chako:ra birds
   c. rays of light
   d. full moon

5. The autumnal clouds in full moon light look
   a. enchanting
   b. weird
   c. mysterious
   d. none of the above

II. Fill in the blanks with Sanskrit words

1. We see Hayagri:va seated on the _____ (navapundari:ke, sarath)

   Moonlight delights the _____ (chako:raha, Chandra)

   Lord drives away _____(thama:msi, _____)
   _____ (mayu:khaihi,)

2. The moon is shining _____ (sarath ghane:, _____)

III. Correct the spellings

1. thamusi
2. visadahi
3. mayuhaihi
4. surath
5. samprimayunthum

IV. Fill in the missing letters

1. ni __ __ : m ___ y ___ :
2. na___ a ____ u ___ ___ a ___ i ___ ___ e ___
3. c ___ a ____ d ____ ___ m
4. ____ h a ___ e ___
5. vi____ ___ s ____ a ____ a

V. Answer the following

1. Why are the scholars happy?
2. What is the food for the scholars?
3. How does Lord enchant our hearts?

VI. Learn More

Vishnu	–	Hey look Goda! Grandma is pouring flour on the ground!
Goda	–	She is not pouring flour. She is decorating the entrance with 'muggulu'. Yesterday, I was told that these "muggulu" are auspicious and become food for small insects!
Vishnu	–	Wow! That is very compassionate!
Grandma	–	Our ancestors were really concerned and compassionate towards all creatures. Hence, they started this practice to feed small insects, birds etc.
Goda	–	Then, they can also live in harmony with us.
Grandma	–	Exactly! You are right. We are living not because of our own efforts, but because all these birds, animals and insects are helping us in many ways. Drawing "muggulu" adds beauty to the house, improves our skills, connects us with neighbours, and helps other creatures to live.
Vishnu	–	Grandma, but why are you drawing birds in the muggulu?
Goda	–	What birds are they?
Grandma	–	These are parrots!
Vishnu	–	Why parrots? Why not sparrows?
Grandma	–	I learned this muggu from my mother. Ask you grandfather why we draw parrots instead of sparrows. I have lots of work to do. I still need to cook dinner for you guys!
Vishnu & Go:da	–	Grandpa! Grandpa!
Grandpa	–	Calm down children! Whats up?
Go:da	–	Why is Grandma drawing a parrot in the muggu and not a sparrow? Is there any significance?

Grandpa	–	Yeah, sure, why not? Everything has an inner meaning. Parrots symbolize a:cha:ryas. Parrots also represent good speech. A:cha:rya is one who gives us good messages. We draw parrots, to remind ourselves to speak good words as taught by our acharyas.
Vishnu	–	There is a chako:ram in this slo:ka. What about that bird?
Go:da	–	What is a chako:ra bird anyway?
Grandpa	–	This bird's only food is moonlight. Similarly, for a disciple, a:cha:rya's upadesam is food. We should always grow with the knowledge provided by a:charya and not with anything else.
Vishnu	–	Are there any other birds which are significant?
Grandpa	–	Yes! There are many other birds. Birds are commonly compared to a:cha:ryas. Scriptures mention many birds that each reveal certain qualities of an a:cha:rya. By understanding these birds, you will be able to admire a few qualities of a:cha:ryas.
Go:da	–	Can you name a few birds grandpa?
Grandpa	–	Sure. Cha:thaka, swan, peacock, cuckoo, crow, hen. Can you find out how these birds relate to a:cha:ryas?
Vishnu	–	Please tell us, we can't do the research.
Grandpa	–	Okay. A cha:thaka collects and drinks only rainwater. Similarly, a perfect a:cha:rya collects knowledge only from the lineage of a:cha:ryas.
Goda	–	Wow! What about a swan?
Vishnu	–	A swan never lives in dirt. It lives only in pure water and drinks only the milk leaving the water behind.
Grandpa	–	Yes, you got it. Better than that, an A:charya eliminates the dirt and makes his disciples pure. Though the world is mixed with good and bad, an A:charya selects only good things for us.

A cuckoo bird is known for its sweet song. A:cha:yas only speak good things for our welfare.

A crow invites all the other crows to come before eating. It never eats alone. Similarly, a:cha:rya shares all good things with his disciples. He never enjoys anything alone.

A hen wakes people on a timely basis. A:charyas also remind us about our duties on a timely basis.

Peacock dances after it sees clouds. Similarly A:charyas feel joy when see their disciples doing good and divine practices.

Vishnu   –   This is amazing Grandpa! A:cha:rya is so great!

Goda   –   Thanks Grandpa! I will make a chart with this information and show it to my friends and classmates.

Questions

1. Draw the five birds using your imagination.

2. Imagine yourself as one of those birds. Write an inspiring short story about your life.

3. Write any slo:ka from Sri:mad Ra:ma:yana which refers to a bird.

4. Quote the slo:ka Va:lmi:ki sang after seeing that the bird killed by a hunter.

5. List three other mythological creatures and describe them.

6. Name at least two English novels that depict mythological creatures.

7. What are the other sources of gaining knowledge other than A:cha:rya?

VII. Solve the puzzle with Sanskrit words for the clues related in the sloka given below

Across

4. one of the seasons

5. scholars

6. like

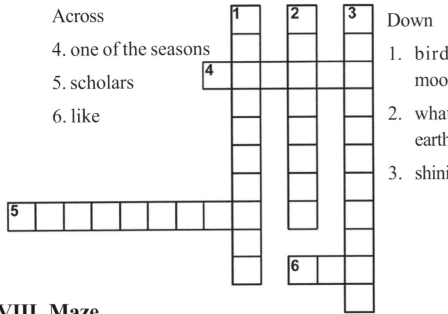

Down

1. birds whose food is moonlight

2. what revolves around the earth

3. shining

VIII. Maze

The chako:ra birds are in the cave trying to get some moon light. Can you help them?

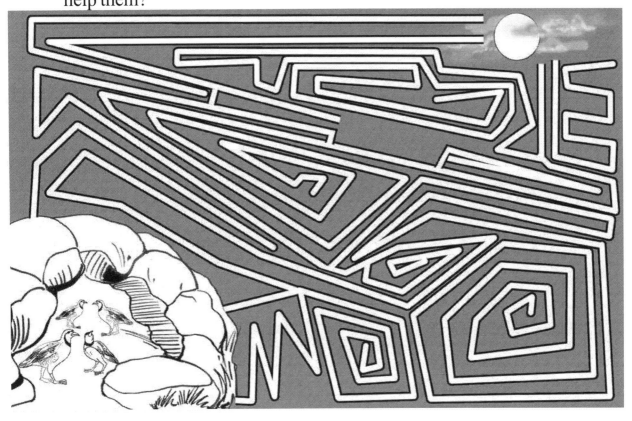

IX.   Do you know?

Season is called 'ruthu' in Sanskrit. Each season is for two months. There are 6 seasons in a year in Asia. The six seasons are -

1)   Vasantha Ruthu (spring)

2)   Gri:shma Ruthu (summer)

3)   Varsha Ruthu (rains)

4)   Sarad Ruthu (autumn)

5)   He:mantha Ruthu (winter)

6)   Sisira Ruthu (fall)

1.   Paint how each season looks.

2.   Which seasons do you like the best?

3.   Name at least two festivals in each ruthu.

4.   Which months fall under these ruthus?

5.   In which ruthu does Hayagri:va Jayanthi fall?

X.   Research

1.   One of the full moons in autumn is called Sarath Pu:rnima. How Krushna is related to this?

2.   What activities are done on this day?

Make a diorama displaying the festivity on this day.

Sloka 27

I. Choose the correct answer

1. Ka:madhe:nu is
   a. a divine cow
   b. a boon
   c. a swan
   d. none of the above

2. Chant this slo:ka for
   a. eloquent and endearing speech
   b. good leadership skills
   c. concentration
   d. memory

3. The flow of words should be similar to sprinkling
   a. nectar in the ears
   b. holy water on us
   c. medicine on us
   d. none of the above

II. Fill in the blanks

1. Lord! Grant me your _____ (disanthu, kata:ksha:ha)

2. Lord's grace follows the _____ (tharanga:ha, ksharanthi:m)
   of compassion.

3. With Lord's grace, our speech is like sprinkling _____ (daya:,
   amrutham) in the ears _____ (samsritha, pumsa:m)

4. Lord! Bless me with the eloquence like that of _____
   (sada:, ka:madhe:nu)

5. Our words should be like Ka:madhe:nu _____ (samsritha:,
   thwadiya:ha)

III.   Fill in the missing letters to form words

1.   Ksh__ r__ ___ t ___ ____ _____ m

2.   S ___ ____ ___ r ___th ____

3.   D i __ a ___ t ___ u

4.   T __ a ___ a ___ ____ a : ____ u cha___ ____ :ha

5.   ____ r o : ____ ____ ___ e ___ s ___ u

IV.   Correct the Spellings

1.   punsam

2.   amutham

3.   kamadhenim

4.   sharanthim

5.   sarsvathim

V. Answer the following

1.   How will the listener and speaker be benefitted by the grace of Lord?

2.   De:sika compared the eloquence to Ka:madhe:nu 's power. Quote the line from the slo:ka in this context.

VI. Solve the puzzle using Sanskrit words for the clues given below

Across

1.   eternal glance

5.   oh! divine Lord

6.   me

7.   grant

Down

2.   always

3.   your

4.   of audience

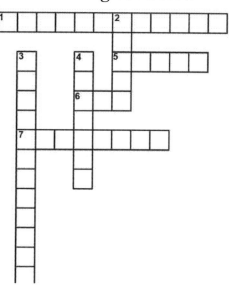

VI. Word Search

```
H U C G K Z H Q J V S S L Y Q
H T F K H Z W P W L J O M C C
M P E T G K S J V E T T K W N
E L A I S O R B M A E N A E P
L M X R J M A B I O P V V L P
G V F O H C O M P A S S I O N
I C X G M D P T A O L C N Q M
N T H G I S P Z M P J C H U E
D R F M T R M U H K H M Y E I
F V E W C I K Q M K S M Z N B
Q N E Q C R W J A C H C G C W
T M J Q L M Q L D I V I N E K
U M U Y N E D T R J N W W V V
A C G I O S C X R E C A H N X
U O A L L H B B B N L V G M B
```

AMBROSIAL

BENIGN

COMPASSION

DIVINE

ELOQUENCE

EMBODIMENT

SIGHT

VII. Learn More (pictures)

Vishnu

& Goda   –   Good evening, Grandpa!

Grandpa   –   Good evening!

Vishnu

& Goda   –   We have a question.

Grandpa   –   Yes. I know that.

Vishnu   –   In Hayagri:va Stho:thram, we keep hearing the word, 'daya'.

Goda   –   What does 'daya' mean Grandpa? Why does it keep appearing?

Grandpa   –   That's a very good question! 'Daya' means compassion in English. Do you know what compassion is?

Vishnu   –   Yeah, compassion means sympathy!

Go:da   –   It comes out of kindness.

Grandpa   –   Yes, exactly. That is what compassion means. Compassion was analyzed beautifully by our a:cha:ryas.

Vishnu

& Goda   –   How do you define 'daya'?

Grandpa   –   There are three stages in 'daya'. Each stage is well defined. The first stage is 'para dukha dukhithwam'. In this stage, a compassionate person drowns in sorrow when he sees others in sorrow.

Goda   –   What is the second stage?

Grandpa   –   He cannot bear the pains of his sorrow.

Vishnu	–	What is the cause for his sorrow?
Grandpa	–	The sorrow of other person. A compassionate person cannot bear the sorrow of others. This stage is called 'para dukha asahishnutha'. This is the second stage.
Vishnu	–	What is the third stage Grandpa?
Grandpa	–	Now, he wants to eliminate the sorrow of others. Otherwise, he cannot be relieved from his sorrow. He puts his efforts to bring them out of their grief. This is third stage called 'para dukha nira:chiki:rsha'
Grandpa	–	Can you think of anyone who has 'daya'?
Vishnu	–	God! Ra:ma!
Goda	–	Lakshmi De:vi too!
Grandpa	–	Excellent! Why don't you make a list of everyone who shows 'daya' and how they show it.
Vishnu & Goda	–	Sure! We're on it right now! Jai Srimannarayana!

Questions:

1. Help Vishnu and Goda finish their list.

3. How does Lord Hayagri:va show his daya:?

4. Do parents have daya: towards their kids?

5. Our leaders should have 'daya:' Do you agree or disagree?

VIII. Maze

Mahesh wanted to go to Ka:madhe:nu to ask for a wish. Can you help him find the way to reach the divine cow?

IX. Project

Create a model of Ka:madhe:nu appearing from the milky ocean during the churning.

X. Research

Find out about a few different varieties of cows.

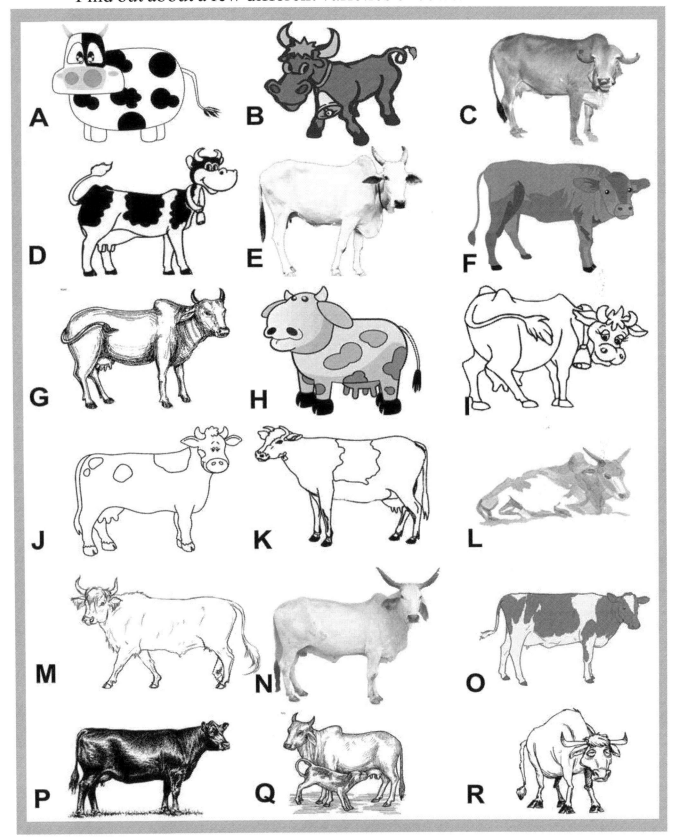

Sloka 28

I. Choose the correct answer

1. We pray lord in this slo:ka to
   - a. reside in our hearts
   - b. reside in our mind
   - c. accept our tongue as His throne
   - d. none of the above

2. We pray to defeat
   - a. weak orators
   - b. feeble debators
   - c. greatest among the poets and logicians
   - d. none of the above

3. The debate area is visualized as
   - a. a huge stage
   - b. a battle field
   - c. a huge stadium
   - d. an open air auditorium

4. The judges and audience participating
   - a. should be highly qualified
   - b. are partial
   - c. have limited knowledge
   - d. none of the above

5. You will be very happy if
   - a. you win against the wisest people
   - b. you win in competitions
   - c. you top the class
   - d. none of the above

II. Fill in the blanks with Sanskrit words

1. Lord! Please occupy my _____ (jivha:gra, nattha)simha:sanam.

2. I wish to conquer _____(pa:ride:shu, kavi:ndra:n) and _____ (tha:rkike:ndran, jihva) in the intellectual competitions.

3. Let there be wise and unbiased judges _____ (viseshavith pa:rishade:shu, jigi:shathaha) .

III. Correct the spellings

1. Natha

2. Vise:shaha

3. Prairide:shu

4. Anganeshu

5. Pamara

IV. Answer the following

1. How should our competitors be?

2. What are the advantages or disadvantages of having well versed, proficient competitors?

3. When are you considered to be a real winner?

V. Unscramble

HAVJI ☐☐☐☐☐

RAGA ☐☐☐☐

SAARAM ☐☐☐☐☐☐

VIAK ☐☐☐☐

HOG:SIT ☐☐☐ : ☐☐☐

VI. Solve the puzzle with English meanings for the words given below

Across

   2. na:ttha

   4. tha:rkika

   5. kavi

   7. simha:sanam

Down

   1. indra:n

   3. agra

   6. jihva

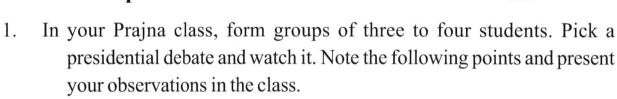

VII. Workshop

1. In your Prajna class, form groups of three to four students. Pick a presidential debate and watch it. Note the following points and present your observations in the class.

   a.   Who are the participants?

   b.   What was their debate topic?

   c.   How long was the debate?

   d.   What are the typical points discussed?

   e.   What is its role in the future of the country?

   f.   How effective was each side in presenting their arguments?

   g.   One who debates well is a good ruler – Do you agree or disagree?

   h.   Are all presidents good at debating?

2. Stage fear is a phenomenon that many people face when speaking to an audience.

a. What do people experience in stage fear?

b. Imagine your friend is about to go on stage to speak in front of a school assembly. He is extremely nervous. What kinds of things would you say to calm him down?

VIII. Comprehension

Vishnu Chiththa was a saintly devotee of Lord Vishnu. He lived during 3000 BC. He was a garland maker. In the temple garden, he used to make thulasi garlands and offer them to the presiding deity Vata pathra sa:yi:.

King Vallabhade:va was the ruler of Madhurai, a nearby kingdom. He conducted a debate to decide who the Supreme personality, worshippable God was. Scholars assembled from all over the country debated for 6 months, but could not come to a conclusion.

He hung a bag containing a huge amount of prize money to the one who won the debate. The prize money was organized in a way so that it would drop down when an authentic debate was presented. However, it never responded. Months passed by.

One night, the Lord appeared in Vishnu Chiththa's dream. He instructed, "Oh my dear Vishnu Chiththa! Go to King Vallabhade:va's court! Reveal to everyone that I, alone, am the Supreme!"

Vishnu Chiththa hesitated, "Lord! I'm not a learned scholar. I don't know any sa:sthras or scriptures. How can I argue before great scholars? How can I prove Your Supremacy?"

Lord decided, " Follow my instructions. I can make a Bramha:sthra out of a grass blade. You do not need to worry. "

Vishnu Chiththa woke up. He went to the king's court in Madhurai. He was well received by the king. He stood before the podium, closed his eyes, saw the Lord in his heart and he meditated upon Hayagri:va. Word flowed from his mouth, quoting various scriptures, and thus established that the Supreme Lord is only one and He is none than Lord Na:ra:yana.

At the instance of his declaration, the bag of prize money fell at his feet. The entire assembly, including the king, was astonished, and happy that issue was resolved.

Vishnu Chiththa was later honored by the King Vallabhade:va in a procession on an elephant. Even Lord Sri:manna:ra:yana, along with Goddess Lakshmi and His entire entourage, came to witness the procession from the skies.

Thus, the grace of Lord is required to be able to debate and win the competitions.

1. Draw a comic strip about this story.

2. Suggest a title for this story.

3. Find out another name of Vishnu Chiththa.

4. Vishnu Chiththa's daughter is worshipped every day. Do you remember who?

5. Name at least three Divya De:sams where Vishnu Chiththa is worshipped.

IX.   Draw

Scholars were gifted with following ornaments by the kings. They are

Kankana – bracelet

Kundala – ear rings

Ganda pende:ram – to feet

Ha:ram - necklace

X.   Spot 10 differences

Sloka 29

I. Choose the correct answer

1. Meditate on this slo:ka
   a. to win in essay competitions
   b. to ace your tests
   c. to win in debates
   d. to win medals in sports

2. Many ignorant scholars
   a. argue using illogical statements
   b. debate about existence of God
   c. try to occupy primary spot with their arguments
   d. none of the above

3. A real devotee
   a. must establish the greatness of God using Ve:dic knowledge
   b. will be blessed by Lord to win in debates
   c. always meditates on Lord
   d. all of the above

4. Ve:das are repositories of
   a. Yajnas
   b. Manthras
   c. Music
   d. Sanskrit words

5. Lord! Bless us to
   a. memorize well
   b. sing your songs
   c. defeat all experts in debate
   d. none of the above

II. Fill in the blanks with Sanskrit words

1. Lord! Let me be glorified in _____. (swa:min, samaje:shu)

2. Lord! Let me become swachhanda ___ ____ _____ su:raha

3. Lord! Let me remember you until _____ (thwanmayatha:m,) prapannaha.

III. Answer the following

1. Write the summary of the slo:ka in your own words.

2. Who tries to establish wrong concepts?

IV. How can we defeat people who argue illogically in debates?

V. Solve the puzzle with Sanskrit words using the clues given below

Across

5. by attaining

Down

1. who instigate illogically

2. by remembering

3. by cornering

4. through Ve:dic mass

VI. Correct the spellings

1. Suraha

2. Vada

3. Dh:amna

4. Samaajishu

5. Sabdamayona

VII. Group Project

Your club wants to start a new VT Seva Debate Class. Create a 3 – fold colorful brochure.

VIII. Color this picture

Ramanujacharya with 1000 heads and debating with 1000 scholars

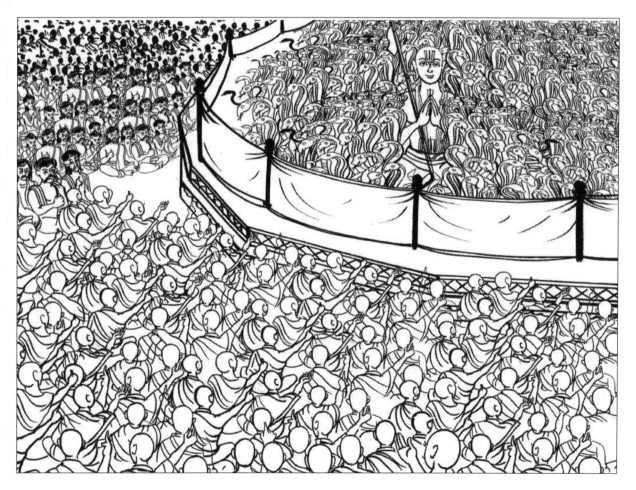

IX.   Workshop

Ask your local VT Seva team for help to hold a debate workshop.

Form groups of four. Each group decides on a topic to debate – two will support the statement to be argued and the other two will oppose it. Your classmates will vote on the side they were convinced by.

Rate your own team's performance. What were the pros and cons of your team? How could you more effectively deliver your side?

After the workshop is over, answer the following questions –

1. What are the qualities of a good debator?

2. Who is a bad debator?

3. Can a good debator have stage fear?

4. How do you prepare for a debate?

5. Is debating a necessary skill for your future?

6. Are public speaking skills necessary for a good debator?

7. List some qualities of a good public speaker.

X. Picture Puzzle

Form the Ashtakshari Manthra "O:m Namo: Na:ra:ya:na:ya" from the repository of Ve:das.

XI. Did you know?

Ra:ma:nuja:cha:rya defeated many atheists at Thondanu:r.

About 1000 years ago, Bhagavad Ra:ma:nuja:cha:rya visited Thondanu:r, in the state of Karnataka, India, which was ruled by King Bittude:vara:ya. The King did not belong to any spiritual path. Influenced by Sri: Ra:ma:nuja:cha:rya, he chose Him as his guru and took the Ashta:kshari Manthra. His name became King Vishnu Vardhana after he adopted Vaishnavism.

The 12,000 athiests residing in the kingdom could not digest the fact that the King had adopted Vaishnavism. They develped prejudice against Sri: Ra:ma:nuja and challenged Him to a debate. To defeat these gurus, Sri: Ra:manuja:cha:rya sat on a Mandapa - a high pedasta enclosed by curtains, and started debating with them from behind the curtain. The atheists were no match against Ra:ma:nuja's arguments. They were also astounded that Ra:ma:nuja was able to debate with 12,000 scholars single handedly.

They peeked inside the curtains, and were shocked to see Sri: Ra:ma:nuja in the form of A:dise:sha with 10,000 hoods, clarifying their doubts and dispelling their ignorance. Even today, we can see this incident recorded on the walls of the temple of Thondanu:r. The picture is also seen in the mandapam where He sat during the debate.

Sloka 30

I. Choose the correct answer

1. Man
   a. has knowledge of all scriptures
   b. is aware of all scriptures
   c. has knowledge of only one scripture
   d. doesn't know all scriptures

2. We should
   a. bow before our gurus
   b. listen to everything our gurus preach
   c. implement gurus instructions
   d. all of the above

3. To get real knowledge
   a. one should surrender before gurus and achieve knowledge
   b. live in a:sram
   c. study in libraries for atleast 14 hours a day
   d. none of the above

II. Fill in the blanks with Sanskrit words

1. Lord! I am ignorant of many kinds _____ (kala:na:m, agathihi)

2. Lord! I did not bow down _____ (dhruvam, thi:rthe:shu)

3. Lord! Aham _____ (ana:ttha, navam navam) pa:thram qualified _____ (daya:ya:ha, dhruvam) of yours!

III. Fill in the blanks to form words

1. Dh___ u_____ _____

2. Pa____ _____ ____ r _____ m

3. ____ a l ____ :n ____ ____ ____

4. V____ d h ____ ____ n ____ : ____

5. N __ v ___ m

IV. Fill in the blanks to form words

1. dh__ ___ v __ ___

2. n ___ ___ ___ m

3. a __ a __ ___ i ___ i

4. d ___ y ___ y___ ___ h ____

5. ____ a ___ a ____ ___ a ____ m

V. Answer the following

1. What is the state of man without intellectual wealth?

2. How can we get intellectual wealth?

VI. Unscramble

PIA

MAHA

RAUVHMD

NAMVA

CAH

AIHITHAG

VII. Picture Puzzle

Identify the different kinds of wealth in the picture below.

VI. Solve the puzzle with sanskrit words for the clues given below.

Across

3. I

5. abandoned

6. qualified

Down

1. at the feet of guru

2. yours

4. of scriptures

II. Workshop

Bhagavad Ra:ma:nuja:cha:rya had many disciples. After finishing their lessons with Ra:ma:nuja:cha:rya, the disciples used to discuss the lessons among themselves to recaptulate and enjoy a:cha:rya's teachings.

Among the disciples of Ra:ma:nuja:cha:rya, there was a dumb and deaf disciple. He used to perform small errands for Bhagavad Ra:ma:nuja:cha:rya. He was very unhappy with the thought that he would never be blessed with the right knowledge because of his physical limitations.

Ra:ma:nuja:cha:rya noticed His disciple's agony. He called him into a room, and closed the doors. Using his hands, with generous gestures, he expressed that reading scriptures is not the only way to gain God's grace. The grace of guru yields much more than the scriptures. Ra:ma:nuja:cha:rya showed His form and asked him to meditate on that using sign language. The disciple was overwhelmed with joy. Tears of joy rolled on his cheecks as he did sasta:ngam. Here is the last manthra from the sixth part of Cha:ndo:gya Upanishad.

yasya de:ve: para:bhakthihi yattha de:ve: thattha gurau |

thasyaithe: katthitha:hy arttha:h praka:santhe: maha:thmanaha ||

Madhurakavi a:lwar is another such disciple who served his a:cha:rya Namma:lvar and attained real 'jna:na'.

Questions

1. List at least two devotees who were blessed by their guru.

2. List devotees who were blessed with knowledge overnight by the grace of God.

3. List the names of three scholars of recent times. How did they become scholars?

III. Picture Puzzle - Identify the scriptures in the picture below

(Scriptures, tom and jerry, whinnie the pooh, etc)

Sloka 31

I. Choose the correct answer

1. There are _____ realities.
   - a. one
   - b. two
   - c. three
   - d. four

2. One of the elements of Nature is
   - a. Air
   - b. Souls
   - c. God
   - d. None of the above

3. Knowing the 3 realities
   - a. makes our knowledge unshakable
   - b. keeps our mind free from doubts
   - c. prevents us from getting carried away by wrong arguments
   - d. all of the above

4. Number of souls is
   - a. Infinite
   - b. Same as the Supreme Soul
   - c. 100,000 million
   - d. None of the above

II. Fill in the blanks with Sanskrit words

1. The eternal concepts beautify madi:yam _____ (prasa:da:th, hrudayam).

2. Thava _____ (prasa:da:th, misinterpretations and doubts will be eliminated.

III. Correct the spellings

1. Bhidihi
2. Mojwalani
3. Samyachi
4. prabahvath
5. Alamkruchiran

IV. Fill in the missing letters

1. Ap_ ni_ th_
2. Bhe_ _ ai_ _
3. Akam_ _ ni: __ __ : n __
4. S __ m y __ n __ ___ __
5. T__ a__ w__ __ __ i

V. Answer the following

1. What are the three realities?
2. What happens if one is ignorant of real knowledge?
3. How do doubts or misinterpretations affect our personality? – there will be no realistic knowledge, our mind becomes ugly, thought process becomes ugly.
4. How can one be free from doubts? – thava prasa:dath
5. What is our prayer to Lord in this slo:ka? – prayer for pure knowledge

VI. Learn More

Kids   –   Jai Srimannarayana Grandpa!

Grandpa   –   Jai Srimannarayana Goda and Vishnu!

Vishnu   –   Grandpa, we learnt about the three realities....

Goda   –   Nature, Soul, and Supreme Soul. Can you please explain what they are?

Vishnu	–	Yeah! Our teacher asked us to create a poster on this topic.
Grandpa	–	This is a wonderful topic. Now, you guys answer my question. Who is God?
Goda	–	The all-powerful one
Vishnu	–	The only one Supreme, master of everyone
Goda	–	who supports everything in this universe
Vishnu	–	by being inside every object and supporting them
Goda	–	as well as surrounding the objects and supporting them!
Vishnu	–	He is Na:ra:yana.
Grandpa	–	You guys are awesome… God is one of the three realities. You already know about Him. Now tell me what is Nature?.
Goda	–	Well, Nature is beautiful scenery
Vishnu	–	Nature is also mountains, oceans, deserts, plains, hills.
Grandpa	–	Good. Almost correct. Now listen carefully: Nature has 5 elements – earth, water, fire, air, space. All the objects we see around are the combination of these 5 elements in different ratios.
Go:da	–	Oh! So… everything we see around like our body, trees, etc are made of these 5 elements?
Grandpa	–	Yes. Nature is called 'açhit' - which doesn't have any life. It does not have any knowledge of its own. This is the second reality.
Vishnu & Go:da	–	What about souls?
Grandpa	–	Souls are us. We exist inside this body. We have knowledge

and are full of life. Hence, we are called 'chit'.

Vishnu	–	What about trees, animals and bugs?
Grandpa	–	Well, their body is product of Nature and a soul exits inside each one of them.
Go:da	–	What about stones, mountains, sand etc?
Grandpa	–	There is a soul inside those objects too. Supreme Lord also exists along with that soul. Because the soul is in a bug's body, it behaves like a bug; if the soul is in the body of a dog, it behaves like a dog. If the soul is inside a mountain, it conducts itself like a mountain and because we are inside a human body, we are supposed to behave like human beings.
		Take any object. The physical form is the result of Nature. Soul and Supreme soul exist inside that object.
Kids	–	Wow!
Grandpa	–	Knowing about these three realities is called Real Knowledge, 'thathva thraya jna:na'
Vishnu	–	We learnt it in Module 2. 'Thrayam' means one which has three things. What is thathva?
Grandpa	–	'Thathva' means reality. Understanding these three realities will release us from the clutches of ego, selfishness, dominance etc.
Kids	–	Thank you grandpa. You explained it so well. We can now make a wonderful poster and get an A on this project.

Questions

1. What are the three realities called in Sanskrit?

2. Who is the Supreme Soul?

3. How many elements do we have in Nature?

4. What is our body made of?

5. Where does soul exist?

6. Where does God exist?

7. What is the advantage of knowing the three realities?

8. What is Nature called?

9. What is a Soul called?

10. Who has knowledge?

VII. Word Search

```
S P A F D U P I L Y E R I K Z
M T U A V X E I P Y J D B N H
M K B R Q Q C M P V L C F O D
A A D U E X A R S U H O I W Z
Y P K G O Z R J O U K S X L I
M I N D V D G S W B U R T E O
W D C M M E K M W P D K B D S
Z B T X Z I H H R X T S H G H
N Y J B S G D E G X M E G E W
Y V A O K L M Q J Z R G V Y D
C C G H S E D M Q T A D B P I
Z N O Y W U D D P V R V C A C
X B U B H J R F T I E X F P M
V I X V F D P N E G O C G X O
R D E R U T A N P O O Y W O F
```

DOUBTS

GRACE

KNOWLEDGE

MIND

NATURE

PURE

SOUL

SUPREME

VIII.   Double Puzzle

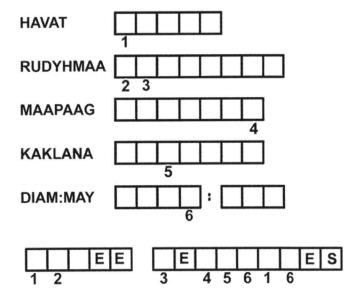

IX.   Group Project

1.   Create a poster on the three realities.

2.   Identify the three realities from the below.

Cow, bird, eagle, oceans, fire, clouds, man, trees, water, Krushna, turkey, lotus, bus, girl, space, stars, moon, Hayagri:va, bread, computers, pens, books, desks, teacher, sun, Lakshmi De:vi, chalks, pencils, mom, dad, soup, comets, tomatoes, airplanes, meteors, sand, comets.

(all have three except avatharas where there is nature and god only.. no soul inbetween)

You already learned about the four types of deficiencies of knowledge in the 5th slo:ka. Under which categories do sanka and kalanka belong respectively?

Sloka 32

I. Choose the correct answer

1. Lord holds _____ in His left hand.
    a. scriptures
    b. lotus
    c. chakra
    d. parrot

2. Lord Hayagri:va glows like a _____.
    a. crystal gem
    b. fresh lotus
    c. white cloud
    d. gold necklace.

3. Lords sits on a _____
    a. pink lotus
    b. white lotus
    c. red lotus
    d. gold throne

II. Fill in the blanks with Sanskrit words

1. Lord, you pundari:ke: _____(pusthakam, nishannaha,

2. You hold _____, _____, _____
   (vya:khya: mudram, pustakam, sankha chakre:) with your lotus like hands.

3. Lord, please emerge(ma:nase:,) _____ and
   soak me with pure and eternal rays of grace.

III. Correct the spellings

1. va:gadhisuha

2. birhath

3. manasi

4. plavayan

5. richure

IV. Answer the following

1. What is the poet's request to the Lord?

2. Describe the form of Lord on whom we have to meditate.

3. How should Lord appear in our hearts?

V. Do you remember

In Module 2, you learnt that Lord resides in your heart as 'Antharya:mi' in Parathva:di Panchakam. Quote the slo:ka.

VI. Solve the puzzle with the Sanskrit equivalents

Across

  4. heart

  6. crystal

  7. who dwells

  8. in a white lotus

Down

  1. never withers

  2. soaking

  3. scriptures

  5. emerge

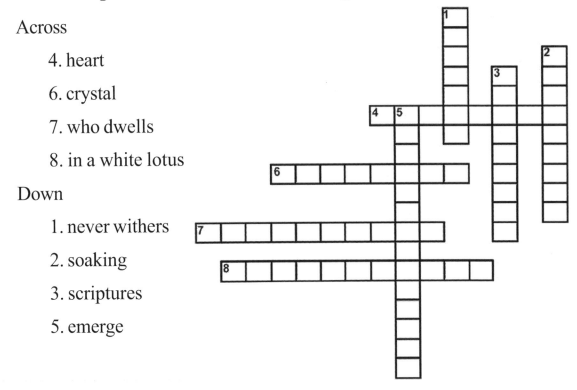

VII. Unscramble

BIANNH   ☐☐☐☐☐☐

HIMMAA   ☐☐☐☐☐☐

TAPIKHAS   ☐☐☐☐☐☐☐☐

RBHBTAHI   ☐☐☐☐☐☐☐☐

MAAM   ☐☐☐☐

HUIHSAIMB   ☐☐☐☐☐☐☐☐☐

SAANAH   ☐☐☐☐☐☐

VIII. Wordsearch

```
L R P N B G D J M E D K L O L
I O L K J E H A M H T M O M R
S P T D I O A A C P F O W B D
D S R U G A M Z O Q K S G Y A
N H E C S V Q G N J B S U C A
E Q M N S K N P C V P O D I B
S P A Z T I G G H B Z L H I T
P P K Z K A D U K S W B W K L
U D T A G E E C R Y S T A L R
K K O R W N G R B W D T Q F F
M S A S G N T V G L K X D M R
E C G O N Q J A T G V D L D M
E T R A E H M D N Z W S A N K
D I B S E R U T P I R C S A V
O I O Z C U A D J B J Y R H D
```

BLOSSOM

CONCH

CRYSTAL

DISC

GRACE

GREATNESS

HAND

HEART

LOTUS

SCRIPTURES

SOAKING

IX. Lord Hayagriva is an ocean on divine qualities. List a few.

X. Complete the picture and color it

XI.   Group Meditation

All of you sit in Padma:sana. Now meditate on Lord Hayagri:va as described in the slo:ka. After the meditation, share your experiences.

XII.   Research

Find Sanskrit terms for atleast 5 divine qualities of Lord.

Sloka 33

I. Answer the following

1. What is the original name of Swamy Ve:da:ntha De:sika?

2. What title was conferred on Ve:da:ntha De:sika?

3. How should one chant the Hayagre:va Stho:thra?

4. What is the benefit of learning this stho:thra?

II. Unscramble

HATRAT ⬚⬚⬚⬚⬚⬚

V:KA ⬚ : ⬚⬚

KAIV ⬚⬚⬚⬚

IIHDDS ⬚⬚⬚⬚⬚⬚

GAARYHI:VA ⬚⬚⬚⬚⬚⬚⬚ : ⬚⬚

III. Research

1. To which period did Swamy Ve:da:ntha De:sika belong?

2. Swamy Ve:da:ntha De:sika's other works.

Slo:ka 26 – 33 Cumulative Exercises

I. Find the odd man out

1.   Souls, supreme soul, earth, nature

2.   Conch, disc, scriptures, jna:na mudra, chanting beads, lotus

3.   Scriptures, a:cha:ryas, gurus, teachers, mother, father

II.   Analogy

1.   27th slo:ka is to endearing speech as 28th slo:ka is to _____

2.   Ka:madhe:nu is to cow and kalpavruksha is to _____

3.   Jihva is to _____ and haste: is to hands

4.   Sankha is to left hand as _____ is to right hand

III.   Match the following

1.ghane	–	white clouds
2.chako:ram	–	chako:ra birds
3.ka:madhe:nu	–	
4.simha:sanam	–	
5.kavi	–	
6.jihva	–	
7.kala:na:m	–	scriptures
8.manase:	–	heart
9.pundari:ke:	–	white lotus
10. pattatha	–	read
11. a:vaha	–	in the war
12. supustakam	–	holding scriptures

LET US ENTRE MODULE 4

Made in the USA
Columbia, SC
14 August 2019